D1080209

ROCK & POP QUIZ BOOK

Over 1000 *Questions*

ROCK POP

& QUIZ

BOOK

from Abba *to* Zappa

Wise Publications
part of The Music Sales Group

Published by
Wise Publications
8/9 Frith Street, London W1D 3JB, England.

Exclusive Distributors:
Music Sales Limited
Distribution Centre, Newmarket Road, Bury St. Edmunds, Suffolk IP33 3YB, England.
Music Sales Corporation
257 Park Avenue South, New York, NY10010, United States of America.
Music Sales Pty Limited
120 Rothschild Avenue, Rosebery, NSW 2018, Australia.

This book © Copyright 2005 by Wise Publications
A division of Music Sales Limited.

Unauthorised reproduction of any part of this publication by any means
including photocopying is an infringement of copyright.

Written and compiled by Lucy Holliday
With thanks to Nick Crispin and Catherine Pate
Cover and book design by Chloë Alexander

Photographs courtesy of London Features International, except:
Nick Drake picture by Keith Morris, Propellerheads picture by David Buchan/Redferns,
Shangri-La's picture by GEMS/Redferns, Jackie Wilson picture by Michael Ochs
Archive/Redferns, SouthPark picture by Paramount Pictures.

All lyrics reproduced in this publication have been approved
by the relevant copyright holder.

Your Guarantee of Quality
As publishers, we strive to produce every book to the highest commercial standards.
Throughout, the printing and binding have been planned to ensure a sturdy, attractive
publication which should give years of enjoyment.
If your copy fails to meet our high standards, please inform us and we will gladly replace it.

www.musicsales.com

Contents

Round 1

Pop Trivia *Part 1*

1 *Who was the first artist ever to top the British charts, and with what song?*

2 *Which major jazz figure was born in 1901 and had chart successes with 'Mack The Knife' (1956), 'Blueberry Hill' (1956) and 'Hello Dolly' (1964), amongst others?*

3 *Which famous film director directed* **Michael Jackson**'s *'Bad' video?*

4 *Which band was originally called Colours, then The Supersonic Bangs, and then The Bangs, before settling on their better known name?*

5 *At which London venue did* **The Smiths** *play their last UK gig?*

6 *Who recorded and released the single 'I Can Hear Music/Goin' Back' under the name Larry Lurex in 1973?*

7 *Which artist is hidden in this anagram?*
I'M A JERK BUT LISTEN

8 *A line from which* **David Bowie** *song gave* **Simple Minds** *their name?*

9 *What are* **k.d. lang**'s *forenames?*

*Who first financed the World Of Music,
Arts and Dance (WOMAD)
festival in 1982?*

From where do the
Average White Band *hail?*

Who wrote the **Elvis Presley** *hit
'Blue Suede Shoes'?*

Which world music group released the album
Laughter Through Tears *in 2004?*

*Who wrote, under the name of Alexander
Nevermind, 'Sugar Walls' for* **Sheena Easton**?

Which Birmingham stadium band consists of
Roy Wood, **Jeff Lynne**, **Bev Bevan** *and*
Rick Price?

Which political party did
George Harrison *fund for the 1992
General Election?*

What is the name of **Kurt Cobain**
and **Courtney Love**'s *daughter?*

Which UK dance act comprises **Felix Buxton**
and **Simon Ratcliffe**?

19 *With with characters did* **R.E.M.** *last perform 'Shiny Happy People'?*

20 *Which folky rock band wrote 'The Glastonbury Song' in honour of the festival?*

21 *Who is* **Sean Lennon**'s *godfather?*

22 *In which year did* **Robbie Williams** *leave* **Take That**?

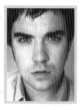

23 *What instrument does* **Roy Ayers** *play?*

24 *'Don't Cry For Me Argentina' by* **Andrew Lloyd Webber** *&* **Tim Rice**, *has been a hit five times. Can you name the artists who have performed it?*

25 *Whose albums include* The Light User Syndrome, Perverted By Language *and* Bend Sinister?

26 *Which record company did EMI buy in 2002 for £42m?*

Pop Trivia Part 1

Who has been an un-credited guitarist on both
*'Hurdy Gurdy Man' (**Donovan**) and*
*'Superstition' (**Stevie Wonder**)?*

27

*Which member of the **Bee Gees***
is the eldest?

28

*Which late member of the **Rolling Stones***
lived in Cotchford Farm, the former home
of author A. A. Milne?

29

To which record producer is
***Shania Twain** married?*

30

Which band holds the title for the
biggest-grossing tour ever?

31

With which former boy-band star did
***LeAnn Rimes** duet on the 2004 single*
'Last Thing On My Mind'?

32

Which 50s crooner had number 1s with
'Don't Let The Stars Get In Your Eyes'
and 'Magic Moments'?

33

Round 1

Pop Trivia Part 1

34 *Which artist first achieved cult status on the strength of two EPs, EP1 and EP2, which he released on his* Twisted Nerve *album?*

35 *On which song did* **Billy Connolly** *base his single 'In The Brownies'?*

36 *Which band started out as* Tragic Love Company?

37 *What did* **Eric Clapton** *study at Kingston Art School?*

38 *What is TV's* **Philip Schofield***'s only single?*

39 *Which band did* **Steve Winwood** *join at the age of 15?*

40 *From which Frank does the group* **Frankie Goes To Hollywood** *take its name?*

41 *Queen's* **Brian May** *received an honorary doctorate in science from which university?*

Who is the son of **George Bellamy**,
the guitarist from **The Tornados**?

What was **Roy Orbison**'s
debut single?

Which single did **The Farm** *re-release
featuring the SFX Boys Choir, for the Euro
2004 football championships?*

What was **Björk**'s *first album called?*

*Which two acts have written hit songs called
'Blue Monday'?*

*Which band holds the world record for Concerts
Performed In Most Continents In 24 Hours?*

Which hip-hop legend discovered **Eminem**?

How many number 1s has
Geri Halliwell *had as a solo artist?*

*Where does the term heavy metal
originally come from?*

1   Al Martino 'Here In My Heart' (November 1952, spent nine weeks at number 1)

2   Louis Armstrong (he also had a UK number 1 hit with 'What A Wonderful World' in 1968)

3   Martin Scorsese

4   The Bangles

5   Brixton Academy (12th December 1986)

6   Freddie Mercury, Roger Taylor and Brian May from Queen (they recorded this while they were waiting for available studio time to work on their debut album. 'I Can Hear Music' is a cover of a Beach Boys song)

7   JUSTIN TIMBERLAKE

8   'The Jean Genie' ("He's so simple minded he can't drive his module")

9   Kathryn Dawn

10 Peter Gabriel

11 Scotland

12 Carl Perkins

13 Oi Va Voi

14 Prince

15 The Electric Light Orchestra

16 The Natural Law Party (inspired by the Maharishi Mahesh Yogi, they believed that yogic flying would help solve Britain's problems)

17 Frances Bean Cobain

18 Basement Jaxx

19 The 'Furry Happy Monsters' (puppets from Sesame Street)

20 The Waterboys (1993)

21 Elton John

22 1995 (July)

23 The vibraphone

24 1976 – Julie Covington (number 1), 1978 – The Shadows, (number 14), 1992 – Sinead O'Connor (number 4), 1996 – Madonna (number 12), 1996 – Mike Flowers Pops (number 3)

25 The Fall

26   Mute

27   Jeff Beck

28   Barry (born in 1947)

29   Brian Jones

30   John "Mutt" Lange

31   The Rolling Stones *Voodoo Lounge* World Tour in 1994 ($121.2m).
      In second place is Bruce Springsteen *The Rising* Tour in 2002/3 ($115.9m)

32   Ronan Keating

33   Perry Como

34   Badly Drawn Boy

35   'In The Navy' (Village People, 1979)

36   Stereophonics

37   Stained glass design

38   'Close Every Door' (from *Joseph* – number 27, 1992)

39   The Spencer Davies Group

40   Frank Sinatra (after an illustration in the book *Rock Dreams*, by Guy Peellaert
      which shows Sinatra going to Hollywood)

41   Herts

42   Matt Bellamy (the lead singer/guitarist from Muse)

43   'Ooby Dooby' (1956)

44   'Alltogethernow 2004' (the original single 'All Together Now' reached number 4
      in 1990)

45   Björk (released in 1977 at the age of 11, the album included covers of songs
      by the Beatles)

46   New Order (1983), Fats Domino (1957) (the Fats Domino version has also been
      covered by Cat Stevens)

47   Def Leppard (they played in three continents on October 23rd 1995, starting in
      Morocco, then to London, finishing in Vancouver at 11.30pm on the same day)

48   Dr. Dre

49   Three ('Mi Chico Latino', 'Lift Me Up', 'It's Raining Men')

50   A phrase from William Burrough's novel *The Soft Machine*

Round
2

The 1960s *Part 1*

1

Under what aliases were David Harman, Trevor Davies, John Dymond, Michael Wilson and Ian Amey better known?

2

Jack Bruce *left which band in 1966 to form* **Cream** *with* **Eric Clapton** *and* **Ginger Baker***?*

3

Which band recorded the theme song to the 1966 Peter Sellers film After The Fox *with* **Jack Bruce** *on bass?*

4

How many UK number 1s has **Roy Orbison** *had?*

5

Which classic single, first released in 1969, was originally recorded by Claude Francois, with English lyrics by Paul Anka, and has been covered by **Elvis Presley**, **The Sex Pistols** *and* **Shane MacGowan***?*

6

Who produced the **Bonzo Dog Doodah Band***'s 'I'm The Urban Spaceman' under the pseudonym Apollo C. Vermouth?*

7

What is **Fleetwood Mac***'s only UK number 1 hit?*

*Who launched his show business career
as a child actor in the BBC TV series
Orlando, and was later a teenage model
going under the name of Toby Tyler?*

*Which band released the album
In-A-Gadda-Da-Vida?*

*The lead singer of which band was arrested
in December 1967 for public obscenity,
in 1968 for disorderly conduct and in 1969
for lewd behaviour?*

*Which were the only two self-penned
songs on **Bob Dylan**'s 1962
eponymous debut album?*

*As whom is Roberta Joan Anderson
better known?*

*What are the names of the two instrumentals on
Pet Sounds by **The Beach Boys**?*

*Who had hits in the 60s with the songs
'I Found Out The Hard Way', 'Trouble Is My
Middle Name', 'Black Girl' and the 1964
UK number 1 'Juliet'?*

15

*Which song, originally recorded in 1903 by Harry Lauder, was a number 1 hit for **Rolf Harris** in 1969?*

16

Who was the first white artist to be signed by the Island record label?

17

*Why was the BBC originally going to ban 'Lola' by **The Kinks**?*

18

*For which singer was 'It's Not Unusual' originally written, before **Tom Jones** made it a number1 hit in 1965?*

19

*Why was **Pink Floyd**'s 'Arnold Layne' (1967) banned?*

20

*Which band did ex-**Byrds** members **Gram Parsons**, **Chris Hillman**, **Chris Etheridge** and **'Sneaky' Pete Kleinow** form in 1968?*

21

Who launched his own Direction label in 1968 with the self-written, arranged and produced album Born Walden Robert Cassotto, *the artwork for which he also designed and photographed?*

Which song by **The Beatles** *is based on Beethoven's 'Moonlight Sonata' chord progression played backwards?*

22

Who was originally a member of **The Drifters**, *but left in 1960 to persue a solo career, in which he released the songs 'Spanish Harlem' and the classic 'Stand By Me'?*

23

Which band was originally called **The New Yardbirds**?

24

The Dave Clark Five *had hits with two different songs sharing the same title. What was it?*

25

Who covered 'With A Little Help From My Friends' (originally by The Beatles), taking it to number 1 in 1968?

26

After what was **The Tornados**' *'Telstar' (1962) hit named?*

27

From which country did **The Guess Who** *hail?*

28

Round 2

The 1960s Part 1

29 — *Which US West Coast super-group formed in 1969 with ex-members of* **The Byrds**, **Hollies** *and* **Buffalo Springfield** *respectively?*

30 — *What were the colours on* **John Entwistle**'s *jacket on the cover of* **The Who**'s *My Generation?*

31 — *Which singer-songwriter has written books entitled* Flowers For Hitler *(1964)*, Parasites Of Heaven *(1966)*, *and* Beautiful Losers *(1966) amongst others?*

32 — *Which illness did* **Cat Stevens** *contract in 1968?*

33 — *Who replaced* **Eric Clapton** *as guitarist in* **The Yardbirds**?

34 — *Who was the best man at* **John Lennon**'s *wedding to Cynthia Powell in 1962?*

*Who played piano on the **Hollies** hit
'He Ain't Heavy, He's My Brother'?*

35

*Which rock star had a football career in the
early 60s at Brentford FC?*

36

*Who wrote **Petula Clark**'s 1967 hit
'This Is My Song'?*

37

*Who was the drummer in **The Beatles** before
Ringo Starr?*

38

The Status Quo – *as they were then
known* – *released their debut
album in September 1968,
featuring the Top 10 hits
'Pictures Of Matchstick Men'
and 'Ice In The Sun'. Name the album.*

39

*What was **Cliff Richard**'s first Christmas
number 1?*

40

1 Dave Dee, Dozy, Beaky, Mick & Tich (respectively!)

2 Manfred Mann

3 The Hollies

4 Three ('Only The Lonely', 'It's Over', 'Pretty Woman')

5 'My Way', most famously a hit for Frank Sinatra (it has spent a massive 124 weeks in the singles chart)

6 Paul McCartney

7 'Albatross' (1968)

8 Marc Bolan

9 Iron Butterfly (1968)

10 Jim Morrison (The Doors)

11 'Talkin' New York' and 'Song To Woody'

12 Joni Mitchell

13 'Pet Sounds' and 'Let's Go Away For A While' (1966)

14 The Four Pennies

15 'Two Little Boys'

16 John Martyn (in 1967)

17 Because of the reference to 'Coca-Cola' which had to be changed to 'cherry cola'

18 Sandie Shaw

19 Because of its lyrical content about a man who stole knickers from washing lines

20 The Flying Burrito Brothers

21 Bobby Darin

22 'Because' (from *Abbey Road*, 1969)

23 Ben E King

24 Led Zeppelin

25 'Everybody Knows' (the first a number 37 hit in 1965, the second a number 2 hit in 1967)

26 Joe Cocker

27 The American communications satellite launched on July 10, 1962

28 Canada (Winnipeg)

29 Crosby, Stills, Nash & Young

30 Red, white and blue (it is a Union Jack jacket)

31 Leonard Cohen

32 Tuberculosis

33 Jeff Beck

34 Brian Epstein (who reportedly wanted to keep the marriage a secret as he didn't want to ruin John's rock star image)

35 Elton John

36 Rod Stewart

37 Charlie Chaplin

38 Pete Best

39 *Picturesque Matchstickable Messages*

40 'I Love You' (1960)

Round **3**

Film & TV *Part 1*

1. *What is the best selling soundtrack of all time?*

2. *Who was the first Afro-American composer to win an Oscar?*

3. *In which soap opera did* **Davy Jones** *of* **The Monkees** *star as a child actor?*

4. *Which film featured* **Bob Dylan**'s *Oscar-winning 'Things Have Changed' in its soundtrack?*

5. *Why does early TV footage only show* **Elvis Presley** *performing from the waist up?*

6. *Which two James Bond theme songs were sung by* **Shirley Bassey**?

7. *Which track by* **Aqua** *was the leading song for the film* Sliding Doors?

8. *In 1979,* **Bette Midler** *played a character in the film* The Rose, *which is based on which singer's life?*

9. *Which British singer wrote and performed the soundtrack to the film* About A Boy?

*In which cult film did **Toni Basil** play a prostitute before her singing career took off?*

10

Which band performed 'Take My Breath Away' featured in the film Top Gun?

11

*Which song by **Oasis** was used as the theme tune for* The Royle Family?

12

2003's Cold Mountain *featured which musician playing the part of Georgia?*

13

*In which US 80s TV show did **Janet Jackson** play a dancer, before making it as a solo artist?*

14

*Which horror film features 'Love Song For A Vampire' by **Annie Lennox**?*

15

Which singer played the great train robber Buster Edwards in the 1988 film Buster?

16

*Which song by **Elton John** was sung by **Ewan McGregor** in the film* Moulin Rouge?

17

Which three former Neighbours *stars have had UK number 1 singles?*

18

19 *The* **Sneakers Pimps**' *album* Becoming X *featured a version of 'How Do' which appeared in which cult 1973 film?*

20 *Which actor played* **Sid Vicious** *in the film* Sid And Nancy: Love Kills?

21 **Prince***'s 'Good Love' appeared on the soundtrack to which 1988 film?*

22 *Steve Coogan playing* **Tony Wilson**, *Ralf Little playing* **Peter Hook**, *Danny Cunningham playing* **Shaun Ryder** *and Mark Windows playing* **Johnny Rotten** – *name the film.*

23 **David Bowie** *provided the song 'Underground' for which 80s film (in which he also starred)?*

24 *The members of which Irish band all featured in the 1991 film* The Commitments?

25 *With which high-pitched songstress did* **Whitney Houston** *duet on 'When You Believe' from the* Prince Of Egypt *soundtrack in 1998?*

26 *Which vocalist appeared in the films* Catch-22 *in 1969, and* Carnal Knowledge *in 1971?*

Which song by **Maria McKee** *was taken from the soundtrack to* Days Of Thunder?

Which pop group starred in the 2003 film Seeing Double?

Who recorded the TV theme song for In Sickness And In Health?

Which **Joni Mitchell** *song did* **Counting Crows** *cover for the film* Two Weeks Notice?

In which play did **Bob Dylan** *make his UK TV debut?*

How many songs from **The Beatles**' *album* A Hard Day's Night *featured in the film of the same name?*

With which song did Neighbours actor **Stefan Dennis** *have a hit in 1989?*

Which all girl group was on the soundtrack and was also seen performing on Tarantino's Kill Bill Vol. 1?

In how many fictional films did **Elvis Presley** *star between 1956 and 1969?*

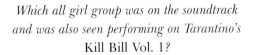

36 *Which singer-songwriter has had bit parts in* Married To The Mob *and* The Silence Of The Lambs?

37 *Which spoof rock group wrote the songs 'Bitch School', 'Big Bottom' and 'Hell Hole'?*

38 *What was the vocal version of the* Eastenders *theme tune called, and who sang it?*

39 *Which song is featured during the opening sequence of* Withnail and I?

40 *Who had a number 2 hit in 1985 with 'Axel F', which featured in the film* Beverley Hills Cop?

41 **Ewan McGregor**'s *role in* Velvet Goldmine *is based on which rocker?*

42 *Which female singer played* **Jean Harlow** *in 2004's* The Aviator?

43 *With whom did* **Rufus Wainwright** *duet on the song 'I Eat Dinner' from the soundtrack to* Bridget Jones: Edge of Reason?

Who was the lead singer of the little known 80s band **Oingo Boingo***, and is now a hugely successful composer for film and television?*

44

Which **Dandy Warhols** *song was featured in the Vodafone TV commercial in 2001?*

45

Which diva starred in the film Beaches, *and released the single 'Wind Beneath My Wings' for the film soundtrack?*

46

Which band re-recorded 'Sympathy For The Devil' in 1995 from the film Interview With The Vampire?

47

Who had a number 6 hit in 1984 with 'Footloose' featured in the film of the same name?

48

What was the title of the BBC programme aired on 1st June 1963 dedicated to **The Beatles***?*

49

In the TV sitcom Friends, *which female rock star was taught by Pheobe to sing the 'Smelly Cat Song'?*

50

Round 3

Answers

1   *Saturday Night Fever*

2   Isaac Hayes (for his score of *Shaft*)

3   *Coronation Street* (in 1956, he played Ena Sharples' grandson at the age of 11)

4   *Wonder Boys* (2001)

5   Because it was thought by producers of the *Ed Sullivan Show* in 1957 that his hip swinging was too suggestive

6   'Goldfinger' (1964) and 'Diamonds Are Forever' (1972)

7   'Turn Back Time' (number 1 in 1998)

8   Janis Joplin (Midler played the part of Mary Rose Foster)

9   Badly Drawn Boy

10 *Easy Rider*

11 Berlin (number 1 in 1986)

12 'Half The World Away' (from the album *The Masterplan*)

13 Jack White (he also performed a number of songs on the soundtrack)

14 *Fame* (1982)

15 *Bram Stoker's Dracula*

16 Phil Collins

17 'Your Song'

18 Jason Donovan, Kylie Minogue and Holly Valance

19 *The Wicker Man*

20 Gary Oldman (1986)

21 *Bright Lights, Big City*

22 *24 Hour Party People* (2002)

23 *Labyrinth*

24 The Corrs (Andrea Corr played Jimmy Rabbitte's sister, and the others all had bit parts)

25 Mariah Carey

26   Art Garfunkel

27   'Show Me Heaven'

28   S Club

29   Chas & Dave

30   'Big Yellow Taxi' (featuring Vanessa Carlton)

31   *Madhouse On Castle Street*

32   Seven (out of 13. The film features 'A Hard Day's Night', 'I Should Have Known Better', 'If I Fell', 'I'm Happy Just To Dance With You', 'And I Love Her', 'Tell Me Why' and 'Can't Buy Me Love')

33   'Don't It Make You Feel Good' (reaching number 16)

34   The 5.6.7.8's

35   31 (he also starred in two documentaries)

36   Chris Isaak

37   Spiñal Tap

38   'Anyone Can Fall In Love' (Anita Dobson in 1986)

39   'A Whiter Shade of Pale' (Procol Harum) as King Curtis

40   Harold Faltermeyer

41   Iggy Pop

42   Gwen Stefani

43   Dido (the song was written by Kate McGarrigle, Wainwright's mother)

44   Danny Elfman

45   'Bohemian Like You'

46   Bette Midler

47   Guns N' Roses

48   Kenny Loggins

49   *Pop Go The Beatles*

50   Chrissie Hynde

The 1970s *Part 1*

1. *In which year did **ABBA** win the Eurovision song contest with 'Waterloo'?*

2. *Which **Chuck Berry** song did Mary Whitehouse protest about, suggesting that the BBC was using the song "as a vehicle for mass child molestation?"*

3. *What was the **Jackson Five**'s debut single?*

4. *Who started out in a 70s punk band The Nipple Erectors (later shortened to The Nips)?*

5. *Which band released an EP titled An Ideal For Living in 1977 on their own Enigma label, on which the fold-out sleeve was inscribed with the legend: "This is not a record – it is an enigma"?*

6. *How old was **Little Jimmy Osmond** when he had his first, and only, number 1 in 1972 with 'Long Haired Lover From Liverpool'?*

7. *What is the final song on **Lou Reed**'s Transformer?*

8

Which is the only album by **The Who** *to hit the UK number 1 spot?*

9

Who painted the album cover for So Far *by* **Crosby, Stills, Nash & Young***?*

10

Which song by **The Faces** *holds the record for the longest title of a hit single?*

11

Which band was formed by ex-members of **Nice***,* **King Crimson** *and* **Atomic Rooster** *in 1970?*

Which song did **Kate Bush** *write at just 13 years old, which later became a hit from her 1978 album* The Kick Inside*?*

12

Who played organ, piano, celeste, cello, viola and harpsichord on **Nick Drake's** *1970* Bryter Layter *album; produced acclaimed debut albums by* **The Stooges** *(1969's self titled album),* **Patti Smith** *(1975's* Horses*),* **The Modern Lovers** *(1976's* The Modern Lovers*) and* **Squeeze** *(1978's* Squeeze*); and released seven studio albums between 1970 and 1975 in his own right?*

13

Round
4

The **1970s** Part 1

*Which song took **Alvin Stardust** to the top of the UK charts in 1974?*

14

Who had a Top 10 hit album on both sides of the Atlantic with the 1972 release Caravanserai?

15

*Which **Queen** song was based on a Richard Dadd painting of the same name and is exhibited in London's Tate Britain art gallery?*

16

*Which charity concert did **George Harrison** organise in Madison Square Garden, New York 1971?*

17

Which duo won Best International Single, and Best International Album at the very first Brit Awards in 1977, and with which song?

18

Which band started out as The Stilettoes, then became Angel, then Snakes, before deciding on their now better-known name?

19

*What was the name of the book written by **Bob Dylan** in 1970?*

20

Which band started out as
Soft White Underbelly, is an anagram of
CULLY STOUT BEER, and has a logo that is
the ancient symbol of Cronos, the Titan God,
who ate his son, the Grim Reaper?

21

Which instrument did **Steven Tyler**
play when he first joined
Aerosmith *in 1970?*

22

Which is considered to be the first pop video to
incorporate both live action and animation?

23

Which song was put with 'Mull Of Kintyre'
to make it a double-A-side?

24

Who produced **Nilsson**'s *1974 album*
Pussycats?

25

How many songs did the 1974
album Having Fun With Elvis
On Stage *feature?*

26

Who was named after a pet hamster and a
Lou Reed *song?*

27

Round 4

The 1970s Part 1

28 *Which is the only album by* **The Police** *not to make it to the UK number 1 spot (excluding compilation/best of albums)?*

29 *Whose final hit of the '70s was titled 'The Soul Of My Suit'?*

30 *In 1970, with just one single remaining on their Decca contract,* **The Rolling Stones** *offered a song that the label refused to release (and has never officially been made available). What was the song?*

31 *Which punk band supported* **Adam & The Ants** *in 1975 for their first gig at London's St Martin's School Of Art?*

32 *Which* **Carole King** *song did* **James Taylor** *chart with in 1971?*

33 *Which single launched* **Diana Ross'** *solo career in 1970, and became a US number 1?*

Who covered **John Martyn**'s
'May You Never' in 1977?

34

Who performed with **Robert Plant**
on the **Led Zeppelin** *ballad*
'The Battle Of Evermore' in 1971?

35

*Who received the 1979 Grammy award
for best disco recording?*

36

About which event was
Deep Purple's *'Smoke On
The Water' written?*

37

Which female singer published the book
And A Voice To Sing With *in 1978?*

38

Who was the lead vocalist in **Genesis** *before*
Phil Collins *took over?*

39

Who is the female vocalist on **Pink Floyd**'s
'The Great Gig In The Sky'?

40

Round 4

Answers

1   1974

2   'My-Ding-A-Ling' (1972)

3   'I Want You Back' (number 1 in 1970)

4   Shane MacGowan (they released an album called *Only The End Of The Beginning*, with MacGowan going under the name Shane O'Hooligan)

5   Joy Division

6   Nine

7   'Goodnight Ladies'

8   *Who's Next* (1971)

9   Joni Mitchell

10   'You Can Make Me Dance, Sing Or Anything Even Take The Dog For A Walk, Mend A Fuse, Fold Away The Ironing Board Or Any Other Domestic Short Coming' (reaching number 12 in 1974)

11   Emerson, Lake & Palmer

12   'The Man With The Child In His Eyes'

13   John Cale (former member of The Velvet Underground)

14   'Jealous Mind'

15   Santana

16   'The Fairy Feller's Master Stroke'

17   Concert for Bangladesh (featuring performances by Eric Clapton, Bob Dylan, Ravi Shankar and many more)

18   Simon & Garfunkel 'Bridge Over Troubled Water' (the song also won six Grammy awards)

19   Blondie

20   *Tarantula*

21   Blue Öyster Cult

22   Drums (he left, and rejoined later as lead singer)

23   'Another Brick In The Wall (Part II)' (Pink Floyd, 1979)

24   'Girls' School' (Wings 1977)

25   John Lennon

26   None, it was comprised solely of Presley's between-song stage patter

27   Sid Vicious (John Lydon named him 'Sid' after his pet hamster, and 'Vicious' after the Lou Reed song of the same name)

28   *Outlandos D'amour* (number 6 in 1979). (*Reggatta De Blanc, Zenyatta Mondatta, Ghost In The Machine* and *Synchronicity* all hit the UK number 1 spot)

29   T. Rex (reaching number 42 in April 1977, five months before the front man Marc Bolan was killed in a car crash on September 16th)

30   'Cocksucker Blues' (later the title of a 1972 tour documentary on the Stones)

31   The Sex Pistols

32   'You've Got A Friend' (his biggest UK hit)

33   'Ain't No Mountain High Enough'

34   Eric Clapton (the version appeared on his *Slowhand* album)

35   Sandy Denny

36   Gloria Gaynor – 'I Will Survive'

37   The fire at the Montreux Casino, Switzerland, 3 December 1971. (The fire was started by a flare gun during a Zappa concert, at which Deep Purple were the support act)

38   Joan Baez

39   Peter Gabriel (who left in 1975)

40   Clare Torry

Pop Trivia *Part 2*

1 *What is the best selling Christmas song ever, and who performed it?*

2 *How old was* **Michael Jackson** *when his career started?*

3 *At the very first Q Awards ceremony in 1990, which band received the Best Album award, with their record* Goodbye Jumbo?

4 *What was the first single released by the 13-year-old country star* **Dolly Parton**?

5 *From which 1982 album do the songs 'India', 'Take A Chance With Me' and 'More Than This' come?*

6 *Who did* **Rod Stewart** *marry in 1975?*

7 *Whose real name is Cherilyn Sarkasian LaPier?*

8 *Which 50s pianist had 22 top 20 hits (including two number 1s), and also performed 'Black & White Rag' which is now used as the theme to* Pot Black?

9 *What nationality is the electronica duo* **Air**?

*Name the two collective recording
and production alter egos of
Pharrell Williams and Chad Hugo.*

10

*What was the written message that
appeared for a split-second in
Prince's video for 'Alphabet Street'?*

11

*Who was the first female Canadian artist
to top the US album charts?*

12

*Who originally recorded 'Up Where We Belong'
before it was a number 7 hit for
Joe Cocker & **Jennifer Warnes**?*

13

*Who played keyboard on 'Get Back' by
The Beatles?*

14

*Who painted the portrait of Nipper the dog,
which was bought by the Gramophone Company
in 1899 and used on the British
His Masters Voice record labels?*

15

*Which Christmas song was sung by
The Waitresses, and was later covered by the
Spice Girls as a B side?*

16

*Who did **Whitney Houston** marry in 1992?*

17

*Which musical did **ABBA**'s Björn and Benny
write, with lyrics by Tim Rice?*

18

Round 5

19 *Which song by **Prodigy** was condemned for encouraging violence, and was only allowed to be played after the 9 o'clock watershed?*

20 *Who, at the height of his career, took a degree and became a minister in the Seventh Day Adventist church?*

21 *Which singer songwriter contributed two song lyrics for* Songs From Liquid Days *by **Philip Glass**?*

22 *How does the German word **Kraftwerk** translate into English?*

23 *Which rap crew is made up of **Ice Cube**, **Eric 'Eazy-E' Wright**, **MC Ren**, **Dr Dre** and **DJ Yella**?*

24 *Which film director did **Madonna** marry in November 2000?*

25 *Which pop star caused a media uproar in January 1997, when he gave an interview saying positive things about the drug ecstasy?*

26 *With whom did **Stevie Wonder** collaborate on the song 'My Love'?*

27 *Who was the original drummer in **Genesis**?*

With whom did **Chrissie Hynde** *have a child, before dating* **Jim Kerr** *of* **Simple Minds**?

28

Who was the headlining act at the first ever Glastonbury music festival in 1970?

29

Which rock band has **Nikki Sixx** *formed since* **Mötley Crüe** *disbanded?*

30

Who wrote both 'Rockin' Around The Christmas Tree' and 'Rudolph The Red-Nosed Reindeer'?

31

With which opera singer did **Freddie Mercury** *duet on the song 'Barcelona'?*

32

Who originally duetted with **Sarah Brightman** *on the single 'Phantom Of The Opera' only to be usurped by* **Michael Crawford** *for the lead in the musical?*

33

How many Grammys did **Carlos Santana** *win in 2000, equalling* **Michael Jackson**'s *1984 record?*

34

Who was Britain's first independent record producer?

35

Round 5

36 *From what instrument did* **Bo Diddley** *take his name?*

37 *Which artist has written a book called* The Modern Antiquarian?

38 *Which band is named after the state of perfect blessedness attained through the annihilation of the self, the cycle of reincarnation?*

39 *In which year was* **Sinead O'Connor** *ordained into the Latin Tridentine Church?*

40 *Who worked as a session musician in the late 80s under the pseudonym Romeo Blue, before embarking on a solo career?*

41 *Who released an album in 2004 entitled* Destroy Rock And Roll?

42 *Who, in 1999, released a remix of* **Bob Marley***'s 'Sun Is Shining', reaching number 3 in the UK charts?*

43 *Which band penned the Ibiza club anthem 'Café Del Mar'?*

About which artist did **Leonard Cohen** *write his classic song 'Chelsea Hotel' about?*

44

Which high pitched singer co-wrote 'Lay Down Sally' with **Eric Clapton***, under her real name Marcy Levy?*

45

Which artist is hidden in this anagram?
NIP YER BREAST

46

Who originally had a US number 1 with 'Venus' in 1970, later to be covered by **Bananarama** *in 1986?*

47

In which year was the first Now That's What I Call Music *compilation album released?*

48

Which 1999 **Bowie** *album was the first by a major artist to be made available as an internet download?*

49

What is currently the most valuable jazz instrument in the world?

50

1   'White Christmas', sung by Bing Crosby (this song was originally sung in the 1942 movie *Holiday Inn*. To date this single has sold over 30 million copies world wide)

2   11 (with the Jackson 5)

3   World Party

4   Puppy Love

5   *Avalon* (Roxy Music)

6   Britt Eckland

7   Cher

8   Winifred Atwell

9   French

10   N*E*R*D and The Neptunes

11   "Don't buy The Black Album. I'm sorry"

12   Alanis Morissette (*Jagged Little Pill*, 1995)

13   Buffy Saint-Marie

14   Billy Preston

15   Francis Barraud (the picture is still used today by HMV)

16   'Christmas Wrapping'

17   Bobby Brown

18   *Chess*

19   'Smack My Bitch Up' (1997)

20   Little Richard

21   Suzanne Vega

22   Power Plant

23   N.W.A

24   Guy Ritchie

25   Brian Harvey (East 17)

26   Julio Iglesias (reaching number 5 in 1988)

27	Chris Stewart (replaced by Phil Collins in 1970)
28	Ray Davies (The Kinks)
29	Marc Bolan & T. Rex
30	Brides Of Destruction
31	Johnny Marks
32	Montserrat Caballe (in 1992)
33	Steve Harley (Cockney Rebel)
34	Eight. (1) Album Of The Year - *Supernatural*, (2) Record Of The Year –'Smooth', (3) Best Pop Performance By A Duo Or Band – 'Maria Maria' (4) Best Pop Instrumental Performance – 'El Farol', (5) Best Pop Collaboration With Vocals – 'Smooth' with Rob Thomas (6) Best Rock Performance By A Duo Or Group With Vocal – 'Put Your Lights On' with Everlast, (7) Best Rock Instrumental Performance – 'The Calling' feat. Eric Clapton (8) Best Rock Album – *Supernatural*
35	Joe Meek
36	A one string African guitar
37	Julian Cope (the book tells of Stone Circles and Neolithic sites in the UK)
38	Nirvana
39	1999 (a sect of the Roman Catholic Church)
40	Lenny Kravitz
41	Mylo
42	Funkstar De Luxe
43	Energy 52 (1997)
44	Janis Joplin
45	Marcella Detroit (Shakespeare's Sister)
46	BRITNEY SPEARS
47	Shocking Blue
48	1983 (10th December)
49	*Hours*
50	Charlie Parker's saxophone (which sold for £93,500 at Christies in 1994)

The 1980s *Part 1*

1   *Who was the most successful singles act in the 80s?*

2   *With which song did the* Cast Of Grange Hill *have a number 5 hit in 1986?*

3   *Which was the first* a cappella *song to top the US charts in September 1988?*

4   *To which band did* **Captain Sensible** *and* **Rat Scabies** *belong?*

5   *Who was the female vocalist on the* **Communards**' *1986 number 1 hit 'Don't Leave Me This Way'?*

6   *Which band's first hit was 'Ne-Ne-Na-Na-Na-Na-Nu-Nu'?*

7   *Which New York band consists of* **Posdnous**, **Trugoy The Dove** *and* **Pasemaster Mace**?

8   *Which singer is featured in the 1985* **Eurythmics** *single 'Sisters Are Doin' It For Themselves'?*

In which band was **Tommy Lee** *the drummer?*

9

What has been **Tracy Chapman**'s *only hit single, charting at number 5 in the UK in 1988?*

10

In which band did **Holly Johnson** *and* **Ian Broudie** *first appear before joining* **Frankie Goes To Hollywood** *and* **The Lightning Seeds** *respectively?*

11

Which band set up their own label, Zarjazz Records *in 1985, and had* **Feargal Sharkey** *as their first signing?*

12

How did **Limahl** *come up with his stage name?*

13

Which 80s band released the albums Garlands *(1982),* Head Over Heels *(1983),* Treasure *(1984) and* Victorialand *(1986) amongst others?*

14

What inspired the title for the 1981 **Genesis** *single 'ABACAB'?*

15

16 *Of what material was the sleeve of the* **Durutti Column***'s 1980 album* The Return Of The Durutti Column *made?*

17 *Which song did footballers Glenn Hoddle and Chris Waddle record in 1987, reaching number 12 in the UK charts?*

18 *Which band had a number 1 album entitled* The Raw & The Cooked*?*

19 *Which song writing duo wrote and produced 1988's 'I'm Not Scared' for* **Patsy Kensit** *in her group* **Eighth Wonder***?*

20 *Which band released the albums* Rum, Sodomy And The Lash *and* If I Should Fall From Grace With God*?*

21 *Which* **Elton John** *song is a tribute to* **John Lennon***?*

22 *Which was the first song to get into the British Top 40 with the 'F' word in its title?*

Which band used the following text in their 'musicians wanted' advert for a bassist: "into **Hüsker Dü** *and* **Peter, Paul And Mary**"?

23

Phil Collins *had three solo number 1s in the 80s, 'You Can't Hurry Love', 'A Groovy Kind Of Love' and which other?*

24

A translation of the first lines of which 1986 number 1 song read, 'He was the first punk ever to set foot on this earth, he was a genius from the day of his birth, he could play the piano like a ringing a bell…'?

25

Whose voice speaks the spooky commentary in **Michael Jackson**'s *single 'Thriller'?*

26

The video for 'The Sun Always Shines On TV' by **A-Ha** *was filmed at which English cathedral?*

27

Blondie *singer* **Debbie Harry** *had two UK top 20 singles as a solo artist. What were they?*

28

29

Which group provided the backing vocals for **Donna Summer**'s *'Unconditional Love'?*

30

To which female US rap duo did **Cheryl James** *and* **Sandy Denton** *belong?*

31

What fruit is **Leonard Cohen** *eating on the front cover of his 1988 album* I'm Your Man*?*

32

Why was **Ozzy Osbourne** *banned from performing in San Antonio?*

33

Which singer representing Switzerland won 1988's Eurovision song contest with the song 'Ne Partez Sans Moi'?

34

Who was born Gaynor Hopkins in Wales in 1953?

*From which album did
'Come On Eileen' by* **Dexy's
Midnight Runners** *come?*

35

*Who are Adam Horowitz, Michael Diamond
and Adam Yauch better known as?*

36

Which album by **The Smiths** *was originally
called* Margaret On The Guillotine?

37

Which **Simple Minds** *track is based
on the traditional song, 'She Moves
Through The Fair'?*

38

Which song kept **The Bangles***'
'Manic Monday', written by* **Prince**
*under the pseudonym Christopher,
off the top of the US singles
charts in 1986?*

39

Electronic*'s 1989 debut single 'Getting Away
With It' featured which guest vocalist?*

40

1   Shakin' Stevens (he had four number 1s with 'This Ole House', 'Green Door', 'Oh Julie' and 'Merry Christmas Everyone')

2   'Just Say No'

3   'Don't Worry Be Happy' (Bobby McFerrin)

4   The Damned

5   Sarah Jane Morris

6   Bad Manners (reaching number 28 in the UK in 1980)

7   De La Soul

8   Aretha Franklin

9   Mötley Crüe

10   'Fast Car'

11   Big In Japan

12   Madness (Madness' Cathal Smyth wrote Feargal's first hit 'Listen To Your Father'. After this one hit Feargal signed to Virgin Records)

13   By rearranging the letters of his surname (Hamill)

14   Cocteau Twins

15   It is the chord sequence of the song

16   Sandpaper

17   'Diamond Lights'

18   Fine Young Cannibals

19   Pet Shop Boys

20   The Pogues

21 'Empty Garden' (from *Jump Up*, 1982)

22 'Too Drunk To Fuck' by The Dead Kennedy's (reaching number 36 in 1981)

23 The Pixies (the advert produced only one applicant – Kim Deal)

24 'Easy Lover' (duet with Phil Bailey, on whose album *Chinese Wall* the song appeared in 1985)

25 'Rock Me Amadeus' (Falco. The song was about Mozart)

26 Vincent Price

27 St Albans

28 'French Kissin' In The USA', (number 8 in 1986), and 'I Want That Man' (number 13 in 1989)

29 Musical Youth

30 Salt 'n' Pepa

31 A banana

32 Because in 1982 he urinated on the Alamo. (Osbourne was arrested and charged with defiling a national monument. The ban has since been lifted)

33 Celine Dion

34 Bonnie Tyler

35 *Too-Rye-Ay* (1982)

36 The Beastie Boys (Ad-Rock, Mike D, and MCA respectively)

37 *The Queen Is Dead* (1986. Morrissey recorded a song of this name on his number 1 debut album *Viva Hate* in 1988)

38 'Belfast Child' (1989)

39 'Kiss' by Prince and the Revolution

40 Neil Tennant

Name The Hit *Part 1*

Name the song these classic lines come from:

1
❝ *Mother, can I never come home again
'cos I seem to have left an important part of my brain
somewhere, somewhere in a field in Hampshire.* ❞

2
❝ She sent him scented letters
and he received them with a strange delight ❞

3
❝ *Shock, shock, horror, horror,
shock, shock, horror...* ❞

4
❝ You gotta wrap your fuzzy in a big red bow,
ain't no sum bitch gonna treat me like a ho ❞

5
❝ *Acting on your best behaviour,
turn your back on Mother Nature* ❞

6
❝ Hey Mr Churchill
comes over here to say
we're doing splendidly ❞

7
❝ *I was high on a Molotov of cocktails,
I was low on a hundred things, I was wrong to put my
money where my mouth was, I was right about the
whales and the dolphins...* ❞

8

" *Running down corridors, through automatic doors* "

9

" *I was blind, now I can see, you made a believer, out of me* "

10

" Do you remember dancing in stilettos in the snow... "

11

" *Lucky that my breasts are small and humble, so you don't confuse them with mountains* "

12

" Semolina pilchard climbing up the Eiffel Tower "

13

" *I'm pushing an elephant up the stairs* "

14

" I don't wanna see a ghost, it's the sight I fear the most, I'd rather have a piece of toast... "

15

" Up in Memphis the music's like a heatwave, white lightening, bound to drive you wild "

16 " *We are stardust, we are golden, and we've got to get ourselves back to the garden* "

17 " Jump up, bubble up what's in store? "

18 " I can't tell my friends 'cos they will laugh, I love a member of the staff "

19 " *You scumbag, you maggot, you cheap lousy faggot, Happy Christmas your arse, I pray God it's our last* "

20 " His palms are sweaty, knees weak, arms are heavy, there's vomit on his sweater already, mom's spaghetti "

21 " Riding along in my calaboose, still trying to get her belt unloose "

22 " *With the taste of your lips I'm on a ride* "

" Bagism, Shagism, Dragism, Madism, Ragism, Tagism, Thisism, Thatism "

23

" *I've been talking drunken gibberish, falling in and out of bars* "

24

" Near a tree by a river there's a hole in the ground where an old man of Aran goes around and around "

25

" *So where's the stars? Up in the sky. And what's the moon? A big balloon* "

26

" She keeps Moët et Chandon in her pretty cabinet, "Let them eat cake" she says, just like Marie Antionette "

27

" *The sink is full of fishes, she's got dirty dishes on the brain. It was overflowing gently but it's all elementary my friend* "

28

29

" I'm your only friend, I'm not your only friend but I'm a little glowing friend but really I'm not actually your friend "

30

" Peace came upon me and in peace we weep, so sleep silent angel, go to sleep "

31

" I never said never, ever, you took the words right out of my mouth "

32

" Got rhythm, I can't miss a beat, Got new skank, so reet, got something, I'm winking at you "

33

" Musha ring dum a doo dum a da, whack for my daddy-o "

34

" Look at me standing here on my own again, up straight in the sunshine "

Name The Hit Part 1

66 *We don't talk about love,
we only want to get drunk* 99   35

66 Outside in the cold distance a wild cat
did growl, two riders were approachin',
and the wind began to howl 99   36

66 *I'm the self-inflicted punk detonator,
I'm the one invented twisted animator* 99   37

66 Hey, tell this jerk to take a hike,
there's somethin' 'bout that boy
I don't like 99   38

66 *Hey, hey you're the Monkees, the
people said you monkeyed around,
but nobody's listening now* 99   39

66 *Why must the youth fight against themselves?
Government leaving the youth
on the shelf* 99   40

1 'Sorted For E's And Wizz' (Pulp, from *Different Class*, 1995)

2 'Babooshka' (Kate Bush, from *Never Forever*, 1980)

3 'The Female Of The Species' (Space, from *Spiders*, 1996)

4 'Filthy/Gorgeous' (Scissor Sisters, from *Scissor Sisters*, 2004)

5 'Everybody Wants To Rule The World' (Tears For Fears, from *Songs From The Big Chair*, 1985)

6 'Stop The Cavalry' (Jona Lewie,1980)

7 'Perseverance' (Terrorvision, from *Regular Urban Survivors*, 1996)

8 'Wires' (Athlete, from *Tourist,* 2005)

9 'Movin' On Up' (Primal Scream, from *Screamadelica*, 1991)

10 'Kayleigh' (Marillion, from *Misplaced Childhood*, 1985)

11 'Whenever, Wherever' (Shakira, from *Laundry Service*, 2002)

12 'I Am The Walrus' (The Beatles, from *The Magical Mystery Tour* EP, 1967)

13 'The Great Beyond' (R.E.M. from *The Man On The Moon* soundtrack, 2000)

14 'Life' (Des'ree, from *Supernatural*, 1998)

15 'Black Velvet' (Alannah Myles, from *Alannah Myles*, 1990)

16 'Woodstock' (Joni Mitchell, from *Ladies Of The Canyon,* 1970. Covered by Matthews' Southern Comfort also in 1970)

17 'Love Is The Drug' (Roxy Music, from *Siren*, 1975)

18 'What I Go To School For' (Busted, from *Busted*, 2002)

19 'Fairytale Of New York' (The Pogues feat. Kirsty McColl, from *If I Should Fall From Grace With God,* 1988)

20 'Lose Yourself' (Eminem, from *Eight Mile* soundtrack, 2002)

21 'No Particular Place To Go' (Chuck Berry, from *The Latest And The Greatest*, 1964)

22 'Toxic' (Britney Spears, from *In The Zone*, 2003)

23 'Give Peace A Chance' (The Plastic Ono Band, *Live Peace In Toronto*, 1969)

24 'Sail Away' (David Gray, from *White Ladder*, 2000)

25 'The Riddle' (Nik Kershaw, from *The Riddle*, 1984)

26 'Turn' (Travis, from *The Man Who*, 1999)

27 'Killer Queen' (Queen, from *Sheer Heart Attack*, 1974)

28 'Some Might Say' (Oasis, from *(What's The Story) Morning Glory?*, 1995)

29 'Birdhouse In Your Soul' (They Might Be Giants, from *Flood*, 1990)

30 'The Air That I Breathe' (The Hollies, from *The Hollies*, 1974. The Hollies released two self-titled albums, both are different)

31 'Going For Gold' (Shed Seven, from *A Maximum High*, 1996)

32 'Brass In Pocket' (The Pretenders, from *The Pretenders*, 1980)

33 'Whiskey In The Jar' (Thin Lizzy, from *Vagabonds Of The Western World*, 1973)

34 'Wonderful Life' (Black, from *Wonderful Life*, 1987)

35 'A Design For Life' (Manic Street Preachers, from *Everything Must Go*, 1996)

36 'All Along The Watchtower' (Jimi Hendrix Experience, from *Electric Ladyland*, 1968. Originally recorded and written by Bob Dylan)

37 'Firestarter' (Prodigy, from *The Fat Of The Land*, 1997)

38 'Young Guns (Go For It)' (Wham! from *Fantastic*, 1983)

39 'Big Sur' (The Thrills, from *So Much For The City*, 2003)

40 'Ghost Town' (The Specials, 1981)

The **1990s** *Part 1*

1 *Who was the biggest selling female artist
(worldwide) of the 90s?*

2 *'Baby It's You', released in April 1995, was the first
new single to be released in 25 years by which band?*

3 *Who penned the **LeAnn Rimes** smash hit,
'How Do I Live'?*

4 *Which author joined **Bono** on stage at
U2's Wembley Zooropa gig on
11th August 1993?*

5 *What item is on the back of the **Nirvana** album
Incesticide?*

6 *Which group recorded the album
Do You Like My Tight Sweater? in 1995?*

7 *Which artist co-wrote **Martika**'s second
album Martika's Kitchen in 1991?*

Which song is **Iron Maiden**'s *only UK number 1 single?*

8

Which band formed in 1990 were originally called **Sweet Children** *but changed their name after writing a song about marijuana?*

9

Which traditional tune does 'Never Ever' by **All Saints** *heavily borrow from?*

10

What was the first album by **R.E.M.** *to make it to the number 1 spot in the UK charts?*

11

Who is the female vocalist on **Massive Attack**'s *'Unfinished Sympathy'?*

12

What is the name of **Spïnal Tap**'s *1992 album?*

13

Which band originally recorded 'She's The One' as an album track, later to be a number 1 hit for **Robbie Williams**?

14

15   *With which song did* **Olive**
have a hit in 1996?

16   *Which band did a pastiche of* **The Beatles***'*
Abbey Road *album cover by walking
across the famous zebra crossing in the nude?*

17   *Which guitarist is featured on*
Michael Jackson*'s 'Black Or White' (1992)?*

18   *Who did* **Liam Gallagher** *marry
in April 1997?*

19   *Who duetted with*
Youssou N'Dour *on the single
'7 Seconds'?*

20   *What was* **Blur***'s original name?*

21   *Which* **Rolling Stones** *song did* **The Verve**
sample on 'Bittersweet Symphony'?

Which band has released albums entitled
EX:EL *and* 808:88:98?

22

Who remixed **Suzanne Vega**'s *'Tom's Diner',*
a number 2 hit in 1990?

23

Who features on **Dr. Dre**'s *singles*
'Nuthin' But A 'G' Thang', 'Still
D.R.E.' and 'The Next Episode'?

24

Which **Annie Lennox** *album is made up*
entirely of cover versions?

25

Which **Louis Armstrong** *single was re-issued*
into the charts in 1994 on the back of a
Guinness advert?

26

What is the name of **Black Grape**'s
1995 debut album?

27

How many albums did the
Spice Girls *release?*

28

29

*From which 90s album do the songs 'Glory Box',
'Sour Times' and 'Mysterons' come?*

30

*Which band has released singles under
the names Justified Ancients Of Mu Mu,
and the Timelords?*

31

Who released the album Take Fat And Party
in 1995, and Fat Out Of Hell *in 1996?*

32

Who wrote the
Chesney Hawkes *hit
'The One And Only' in 1991?*

33

What was the title of **East 17**'s *1993
number 1 album?*

34

From which AC/DC song did **Veruca Salt** *get
the name for their album* American Thighs?

*What is the name of the **Cardigans** debut album, and also the name of a long running UK TV soap?*

35

*What was **Kurt Cobain**'s middle name?*

36

*Who recorded 'It Takes Two' with **Rod Stewart**?*

37

*From which county do the **Prodigy** originate?*

38

*Which is the only album by **The Cure** to make it to number 1 in the UK album charts?*

39

*Which **Dolly Parton** song did **Whitney Houston** cover in 1992 giving her her 10th US number 1?*

40

Round 8

Answers

1 Mariah Carey (in the UK Carey released 24 singles between 1990 -1999)

2 The Beatles

3 Diane Warren

4 Salman Rushdie (who had been in hiding for four and a half years)

5 A yellow plastic duck

6 Moloko

7 Prince

8 'Bring Your Daughter... To The Slaughter' (1991)

9 Green Day

10 'Amazing Grace'

11 *Out Of Time* (1991)

12 Shara Nelson

13 *Break Like The Wind*

14 World Party (from the 1997 album *Egyptology*)

15 'You're Not Alone'

16 Red Hot Chili Peppers

17 Slash (Guns N' Roses/Velvet Revolver)

18 Patsy Kensit

19 Neneh Cherry

20 Seymour

21   'The Last Time' (orchestral version)

22   808 State

23   DNA

24   Snoop Dogg

25   *Medusa* (1995)

26   'We Have All The Time In The World' (reaching number 3 in the UK charts)

27   *It's Great When You're Straight... Yeah*

28   Three – *Spice* (number 1, 1996), *Spiceworld* (number 1, 1997) and *Forever* (number 2, 2000)

29   Portishead - *Dummy*

30   KLF

31   Roy 'Chubby' Brown

32   Nik Kershaw

33   *Walthamstow*

34   'You Shook Me All Night Long' ("Knockin' me out with those American thighs...") (1994)

35   Emmerdale

36   Donald

37   Tina Turner (1990 reaching number 5 in the UK charts)

38   Essex

39   *Wish* (1992)

40   'I Will Always Love You' (this was also the lead song from the film *The Bodyguard* in which Houston starred alongside Kevin Costner)

Round 9

Links

1

*What is the common theme in the songs
'Madame George' (**Van Morrison**),
'Rebel Rebel' (**David Bowie**),
'Sheila Take A Bow' (**The Smiths**) and
'Walk On The Wild Side' (**Lou Reed**)?*

2

*What links these three songs: '(Take A Little)
Piece Of My Heart' (**Erma Franklin**), 'I Heard It
Through The Grapevine' (**Marvin Gaye**) and
'Love's Great Adventure' (**Ultravox**)?*

3

What links **The Band**, **Creedence Clearwater
Revival**, **The Grateful Dead**, **Janis Joplin** *and*
Ravi Shankar?

4

What song links **Paul Young** *and* **Chris Martin**?

5

What occupation links **Sting**,
Ian Dury *and* **Bryan Ferry**?

6

*Which event linked these records:
'Stairway To Heaven' (**Led Zeppelin**),
'Live And Let Die' (**Wings**), 'Leavin'
On A Jet Plane' (**Peter Paul And Mary**),
and 'Wipeout' (**Surfaris**)?*

7

*Which two bands both have drummers
named* **Roger Taylor**?

8

Which artist links **Joan Baez**, **Ralph McTell**,
Dire Straits *and* **David Bowie**?

9

What album title connects
Joni Mitchell, **Simply Red**
and **The Mission**?

10

What links **Mark Owen**, **Badly Drawn Boy**
and **Julio Inglesias**?

11

What links the **Pretenders**,
Scissor Sisters, **Seal** *and*
The Rolling Stones?

12

Which word links **Queen** *and*
The Dandy Warhols?

13

What do the albums Kicking Against
The Pricks (**Nick Cave & The Bad Seeds**),
Rock And Roll (**John Lennon**)
and Through The Looking Glass
(**Siouxie & The Banshees**) *have in common*?

14

Who have **Sonny Curtis**, **The Pilot**, **Beat
Buddies**, **Rubettes**, **The Familee**, **Mike Berry**
and **Alvin Stardust** *all written songs about*?

15 *Which two acts have released albums 20 years apart entitled* Kaleidoscope, *one in 1980, the other in 2000?*

16 *Which* Harry Potter *book is also the name of a 1998* **Van Morrison** *album?*

17 *Which two bands released different songs entitled 'New Born' in 2001?*

18 *Which two bands both had number 2 hits with the song 'Wonderwall' in 1995?*

19 *About which event have* **Johnny Cash**, **Kim Wilde**, **Stranglers**, **Stevie Wonder** *and* **Paul Hardcastle** *all performed songs?*

20 *What do the songs 'Chinese Bakery' (**The Auteurs**), '3-Minute Rule' (**The Beastie Boys**), 'Mr Jones' (**Counting Crows**) and 'The Seeker' (**The Who**) all have in common?*

21 *What do the songs 'Guadete' (**Steeleye Span**), 'Only You' (**The Flying Pickets**), 'Caravan Of Love' (**The Housemartins**) and 'Don't Worry, Be Happy' (**Bobby McFerrin**) have in common?*

Which artist do the songs
'Sweet Home Alabama' (**Lynyryd Skynyrd**),
'Highlands' (**Bob Dylan**) *and 'Crème Brulee'*
*(***Sonic Youth***) namecheck?*

22

What album title connects **King Crimson,**
Black Uhuru *and* **The Communards***?*

23

What song links **Marianne Faithful,**
Graham Nash, Jane Asher, Patti Boyd,
Mick Jagger *and* **Keith Moon***?*

24

Which cult film links the songs
'If Six Was Nine' (**Jimi Hendrix**),
'The Pusher' (**Steppenwolf**) *and*
'The Weight' (**The Band**)*?*

25

What album title connects **Def Leppard, INXS**
and **The Beloved***?*

26

What links the songs 'Praise You'
*(***Fatboy Slim***), 'Sabotage'* (**Beastie Boys**),
'Buddy Holly' (**Weezer**) *and*
'It's Oh So Quiet' (**Björk**)*?*

27

28

*Which artist links the songs
'Cold Turkey' (**John Lennon**),
'And So Is Love' (**Kate Bush**) and
'We're Only In It For The Money'
(**Frank Zappa**)?*

29

*Which artist links the songs 'Dream On'
(**Aerosmith**), 'I Got The…' (**Labi Siffre**) and
'Toy Soldiers' (**Martika**)?*

30

Which artist links **Freddie Mercury,
The Pet Shop Boys, Tina Turner** *and*
Bing Crosby?

31

Which two acts have released albums entitled
Angels With Dirty Faces?

32

Which song links **Lulu** *and* **Nirvana**?

33

Madonna, Rod Stewart, Lionel Richie
and **Shaggy** *have all had hit singles with
a song of what name?*

34

Which city links the following acts,
Simple Minds, Boney M, Don Fardon *and*
Katie Melua?

Who links **P J Harvey**, **Drugstore** *and* **Björk***?*

35

R.E.M., **The Pixies**, **Nick Cave & The Bad Seeds** *and* **Lloyd Cole***, have all covered songs by which artist?*

36

Which song by **The Beatles** *was covered in 1965 by both* **Matt Monroe** *and* **Marianne Faithfull***, and again in 1967 by* **Ray Charles***?*

37

In which film are the following songs featured? *'Let's Stay Together (**Al Green**), 'Jungle Boogie' (**Kool & The Gang**), and 'You Can Never Tell' (**Chuck Berry**)?*

38

What links **Elvis Presley**, **The Beatles**, **Cliff Richard**, **Westlife** *and* **Madonna***?*

39

What links **Mott The Hoople**, **Public Image Ltd** *and* **Steppenwolf***?*

40

Round 9

1 Cross dressers

2 They've all been used in Levi's adverts

3 They all played at Woodstock, but non of them appeared in the film

4 'Do They Know It's Christmas?' They both sang the opening lines, Paul Young in 1984, and Chris Martin on the 2004 remake

5 They were all school teachers

6 They were advised not to be played by radio stations following the terrorist attacks on the *World Trade Centre* on September 11th 2001

7 Queen and Duran Duran

8 Bob Dylan, who they've all written songs about: ('Diamonds & Rust'/'O Brother' (Baez), 'Zimmerman Blues' (McTell), 'The Man's Too Strong' (Dire Straits), 'Song For Bob Dylan' (Bowie))

9 *Blue* (released in 1971, 1998 and 1996 respectively)

10 They all nearly became professional footballers

11 They all have had number 1 eponymous debut albums

12 Bohemian ('Bohemian Rhapsody', (Queen), 'Bohemian Like You' (The Dandy Warhols))

13 They are all albums entirely of cover versions

14 Buddy Holly

15 Siouxsie & The Banshees and Kelis

16 *The Philosopher's Stone* (a compilation of rarities and unreleased tracks, also the very first *Harry Potter* novel by J.K. Rowling)

17 Muse and Elbow

18 Oasis and Mike Flowers Pops (the latter's was a cover of the original Oasis song)

19 Vietnam ('Singing Vietnam Talking Blues', 'Vietnamerica', 'Frontline' and '19' respectively)

20 They all name check Bob Dylan: 'Chinese Bakery' – "Just see Bob Dylan on a motorbike", '3-Minute Rule' – "I'm chillin' like Bob Dylan", 'Mr Jones' – "I wanna be Bob Dylan", 'The Seeker' – "I asked Bobby Dylan, I asked The Beatles"

21 They are all accapella top 20 hits

22 Neil Young: 'Sweet Home Alabama' – "I hope Neil Young will remember Southern Man doesn't need him around", 'Highlands' – "I'm listening to Neil Young, gotta turn up the sound", 'Crème Brulee' – "Last Night I dreamt I kissed Neil Young, if I was a boy I guess it would be fun"

Answers

23   *Red* (released in 1974, 1981 and 1987 respectively)

24   'All You Need Is Love (The Beatles) (They all sang in the chorus of the original recording)

25   *Easy Rider* (this was one of the first films to use a soundtrack of previously released material – the most famous song on this soundtrack is 'Born To Be Wild' also by Steppenwolf)

26   *X* (released in 2002, 1990, and 1996 respectively)

27   They all have videos directed by Spike Jonze (who also directed the cult film *Being John Malkovich*)

28   Eric Clapton (he is the featured guitarist on all three songs)

29   Eminem (who has heavily sampled all three in his songs 'Sing For The Moment', 'My Name Is' and 'Like Toy Soldiers' respectively)

30   David Bowie (who has collaborated with all of the above with the songs 'Under Pressure', 'Hallo Spaceboy', 'Tonight' and 'White Christmas/ Little Drummer Boy' respectively)

31   Tricky and The Sugababes

32   'The Man Who Sold The World' (both artists have covered this David Bowie classic)

33   'Angel'

34   Belfast ('Belfast Child', 'Belfast', 'Belfast Boy' and 'Belfast (Penguins And Cats)' respectively)

35   Thom Yorke (they have all recorded duets with the Radiohead front man, 'This Mess We're In', 'El President' and 'I've Seen It All' respectively)

36   Leonard Cohen: (all songs appear on the tribute album *I'm Your Fan*, which is a collection of Cohen covers. 'First We Take Manhattan' (R.E.M.), 'I Can't Forget' (The Pixies), 'Tower Of Song' (Nick Cave & The Bad Seeds) and 'Chelsea Hotel' (Lloyd Cole))

37   'Yesterday'

38   *Pulp Fiction* (1994)

39   They are the only acts in chart history to have 10 or more number 1 hits

40   They are all took their band names from novels (*Mott The Hoople* by Willard Manus, *The Public Image* by Muriel Sparks, and *Steppenwolf* by Herman Hesse)

The 2000s *Part 1*

1   *Who was the winner of 2000's Mercury Music Prize?*

2   *Which three* **Radiohead** *albums went to number 1 in the UK charts in the 00's?*

3   *Which singer performed at the 2004 Olympics opening ceremony wearing a gigantic dress "representing the sea"?*

4   *In which* **Elton John** *video does* **Justin Timberlake** *play a young Elton?*

5   *Which song was 2003's Christmas number 1?*

6   *Of which band is* **Alex Kapranos** *the lead singer?*

7   *How many people are in* **The Polyphonic Spree***?*

8   *Which new band did* **Queens Of The Stone Age** *singer* **Josh Homme** *put together in 2004?*

With which RnB artist did **Chris Martin**
co-write the song 'See It In A Boy's Eyes'?

9

Which band has released albums called
Felt Mountain *and* Black Cherry?

10

*From which album released in 2001
do the songs 'Hyper Music', 'Screenager'
and 'Feeling Good' come?*

11

*Who contributed backing vocals to the
2002 re-recording of 'Danger! High
Voltage' by the* **Electric Six**?

12

Which band did **Pete Doherty** *form after
leaving* **The Libertines**?

13

*Which artist received a Lifetime Achievement
Award at the 2005 Brit Awards?*

14

Britney Spears, **Pink**, **Enrique Iglesias**
*and which other artist appeared in the
2004 Pepsi advert?*

15

16 Which singer has won the Brit Award for Best Female Solo Artist twice, in 2002 and 2004?

17 Which **Gabrielle** song uses the same chord sequence as Bob Dylan's 'Knockin' On Heaven's Door'?

18 In 2001, which was the first Western group to play in Cuba for over 20 years?

19 What does **OutKast**'s 'B.O.B' stand for?

20 Who had a top 10 hit with 'United States Of Whatever' in 2002?

21 Why was the **So Solid Crew** single '21 Seconds' so called?

22 From which 2001 debut album do the songs 'She's So', 'Remind Me' and 'In Space' come?

Which song by **Robbie Williams** *won the Best Song Of The Last 25 Years Award at the 2005 Brits?*

23

Which band has members called **Babydaddy, Del Marquis, Jake Shears, Ana Matronic** *and* **Paddy Boom**?

24

Which British artist covered the **White Stripes**' *'Fell In Love With A Girl' in 2004?*

25

Which ex-Take That member co-wrote songs for **Delta Goodrem**'s Innocent Eyes *album?*

26

Which ex-member of doomed band **Hear'Say** *released the singles 'Cry', 'Come On Over' and 'Sentimental'?*

27

Which group covered **Supertramp**'s *'The Logical Song', taking it to number 2 in 2002?*

28

29

*With whom did **Ozzy Osbourne** duet in his 2003 re-release of 'Changes'?*

30

*Which band covered the classic **Kate Bush** single 'Hounds Of Love' in 2005?*

31

*Which artist is featured on 'Never Be The Same Again', a number 1 single for **Melanie C**?*

32

*In which British band is **Guy Berryman** the bassist?*

33

*With whom did **The Wombles** join up in the song 'I Wish It Could Be A Wombling Merry Christmas Every Day'?*

34

*Which A-list film star duetted with **Robbie Williams** on the number 1 cover version of 'Somethin' Stupid' in 2001?*

Who released an album and single in 2001
entitled 'White Boy With A Feather'?

35

Who holds the record for the fastest selling
album by a female artist?

36

Which pop star sung on and
co-wrote 'Where Is The Love'
by the **Black Eyed Peas**?

37

Which show opened in May 2002 at London's
Dominion Theatre and is based on the music
from one of Britain's greatest bands?

38

Which band released Chocolate St*rfish And
The Hot Dog Flavoured Water in 2002?

39

Which two songs did **Richard X**
put together for his single
'Being Nobody' with **Liberty X**?

40

Round

10

1 Badly Drawn Boy

2 *Kid A* (2000), *Amnesiac* (2001) and *Hail To The Thief* (2003). (*OK Computer* reached number 1 in 1997)

3 Björk

4 'This Train Don't Stop There Any More' (2000)

5 'Mad World' (Michael Andrews featuring Gary Jules – originally a hit for Tears For Fears in 1982)

6 Franz Ferdinand

7 23

8 Eagles Of Death Metal

9 Jamelia

10 Goldfrapp

11 *Origin Of Symmetry* (Muse)

12 Jack White (under the name of John S. O'Leary)

13 Babyshambles

14 Bob Geldof

15 Beyoncé

16 Dido

17 'Rise' (reached number 1 in 2000)

18 Manic Street Preachers

19 'Bombs Over Baghdad'

20 Liam Lynch

21   This was the amount of time each MC had to rhyme

22   *Melody AM* (Röyksopp)

23   'Angels'

24   Scissor Sisters

25   Joss Stone (renaming it 'Fell In Love With A Boy')

26   Gary Barlow

27   Kym Marsh

28   Scooter

29   Kelly Osbourne (his daughter)

30   The Futureheads

31   Lisa 'Left Eye' Lopez (2000)

32   Coldplay

33   Roy Wood (2000)

34   Nicole Kidman

35   Jason Downs

36   Britney Spears with *Oops... I Did It Again*. (Released in June 2000 the album sold 1.3 million copies in its first week of release)

37   Justin Timberlake

38   *We Will Rock You* (Queen)

39   Limp Bizkit (a number 1 album in the UK charts)

40   'Being Boiled' (Human League) and 'Ain't Nobody' (Rufus & Chaka Khan)

Round
11

Pop Trivia *Part 3*

1
Which hit song contains the longest held note, lasting 18 seconds, and who recorded it?

2

Eddie Van Halen *played guitar on which* **Michael Jackson** *hit?*

3
Who are **Paul Hewson** *and* **David Evans**?

4
How many UK number 1s has **Paul McCartney** *had since leaving* **The Beatles**?

5
The first recorded occurrence of the words rock and roll put together, appear in the 20s song 'My Man Rocks Me (With One Steady Roll)'. Who was the original artist?

6
In which year was the first singles charts published?

7
In which year did **Richey Edwards** *of the* **Manic Street Preachers** *disappear?*

8
What is a Foo Fighter?

9
Which **Dire Straits** *song was the first ever CD single?*

What was the UK's first foreign language number 1?

10

In which year did **Bob Geldof** *receive an honorary knighthood for his charity work?*

11

Who was the first white rapper to have a US number 1?

12

Which band won the very first Mercury Music Prize in 1992, and for what album?

13

How many UK top 40 singles did **Nirvana** *have?*

14

For whom did the **Bee Gees** *originally write 'Islands In The Stream'?*

15

With which band did **Mick Hucknall** *first record 'Holding Back The Years' before re-releasing it with* **Simply Red***?*

16

Which band played under the name Bingo Hand Job at a secret European gig?

17

18 *Who said "God had to create disco music so I could be born"?*

19 *With which famous novelist does **Kate Bush** share a birthday (on the 30th July)?*

20 *Which artist is hidden in this anagram? BLAND BOY*

21 *What was special about the 1997 **Lilith Fair** tour?*

22 ***Emmylou Harris'** song 'Boulder To Birmingham' is written about which musician?*

23 *What does record company EMI stand for?*

24 *What was the first album to reach number 1 in 34 different countries?*

25 *In which year did **Elvis** buy his Memphis mansion Graceland?*

26 *Who produced **Band Aid**'s 1984 number 1 'Do They Know It's Christmas'?*

27 *Who is the **Hollies** song 'Carrie Anne' written about?*

Which album inspired Wim Wenders to make a documentary film of the same name?

28

Who made one copy of his LP Music For Supermarkets *and auctioned it for £10,000 in 1983?*

29

*Which **Crowded House** song did **Paul Young** perform at the Nelson Mandela concert, Wembley Stadium 1998?*

30

*Which song by **The Move**, was the first ever song to be broadcast by BBC Radio 1 in 1967?*

31

Which model appeared on the cover of 1973's Pin-Ups *with **David Bowie**?*

32

Which Scottish film composer and pop collaborator won the UK's Young Jazz Musician Of The Year in 1981?

33

Who is known as the 'Funky President', 'Mr Dynamite', 'Soul Brother Number One' amongst other aliases?

34

*Which instrument did **Norman Cook** (AKA **Fat Boy Slim**) play in **The Housemartins**?*

35

Round 11

Pop Trivia Part 3

36 *Which band did **Chris Bell** form with former* ***Box Tops** vocalist **Alex Chilton**?*

37 *How many top 10 albums have the **Pixies** had?*

38 ***Killing Joke** have released two different albums with the same name. What is the name of these albums?*

39 *Which novelist inspired the name* ***Public Image Ltd**?*

40 *In which year was Channel 4's The Tube taken off the air?*

41 *Which artist sang backing vocals on 'Don't Go Home With Your Hard-On'* (***Leonard Cohen***) *and 'All Things Must Pass'* (***George Harrison***)?*

42 *Which guitarist appeared on* ***Frank Zappa**'s 'We're Only In It For The Money'?*

*Who is **Josh Davis** better known as?*

43

How many number 1 albums have **Jamiroquai** *had?*

44

Which vocalist sang the theme tune to the Bond film You Only Live Twice?

45

Which political singer-songwriter helped to form the socialist musicians collective Red Wedge *with **Paul Weller**?*

46

In which year was **Mariah Carey** *born?*

47

With which three countries did the UK share the Eurovision song contest top spot in 1969?

48

*Which saxophonist started his career playing with **Barry White**'s Love Unlimited orchestra'?*

49

Who was the first cover star of Rolling Stone *magazine?*

50

Round

11

1 'Lovely Day', Bill Withers (1978)

2 'Beat It' (1983)

3 Bono and The Edge (from U2)

4 Three ('Mull Of Kintyre' 1977, 'Pipes Of Peace' 1983 and 'Ebony And Ivory' 1982)

5 Trixie Smith (accompanied by the Jazz Masters)

6 1952 (15th Nov)

7 1995 (February 1st)

8 A UFO type object reported by soldiers in WW2

9 'Brothers In Arms' (1985)

10 'Je T'aime... Moi Non Plus' by Serge Gainsbourg and Jane Birkin in 1969 (It was helped to the top spot by a BBC ban)

11 1986

12 Vanilla Ice (with 'Ice Ice Baby' 1990)

13 Primal Scream – *Screamadelica*

14 Seven ('Smells Like Teen Spirit', 'Come As You Are', 'Lithium', 'In Bloom', 'Oh, The Guilt', 'Heart Shaped Box', 'All Apologies')

15 Diana Ross

16 The Frantic Elevators (1982)

17 R.E.M.

18 Donna Summer

19 Emily Brontë ('Wuthering Heights' was Kate's tribute to her)

20 BOB DYLAN

21 It featured only female performers

22 Gram Parsons

23 Electric & Musical Industries Ltd. (It changed its name to EMI Ltd in 1971)

24 The Beatles – *The White Album*

25 1957

26 Midge Ure

27   Marianne Faithful

28   *The Buena Vista Social Club* (1997). By 2005 the album had sold over four million copies

29   Jean-Michel Jarre

30   'Don't Dream It's Over'

31   'Flowers In The Rain'

32   Twiggy

33   Craig Armstrong

34   James Brown

35   Bass

36   Big Star (formerly known as Ice Water)

37   Three – *Doolittle* (number 8, 1989), *Bossanova* (number 3 1990), *Trompe Le Monde* (number 7, 1991)

38   *Killing Joke* (first released in 1980 reaching number 39, the second in 2003, reaching number 43)

39   Muriel Sparks (the band was named after a novel called *The Public Image*)

40   1987

41   Bob Dylan

42   Eric Clapton

43   DJ Shadow

44   Three (*Emergency On Planet Earth* 1993, *Synkronized* 1999, *A Funk Odyssey* 2001)

45   Nancy Sinatra

46   Billy Bragg

47   1970 (in New York, USA)

48   France, Netherlands and Spain. The UK entry was 'Boom-Bang-A-Bang' by Lulu

49   Kenny G

50   John Lennon (he was also photographed for the cover of *Rolling Stone* magazine the day he was assassinated in 1980)

Odd One Out

Who is the Odd One Out in each group?

1

2

1: ABBA/Rod Stewart/Queen/Cliff Richard
2: Janis Joplin/Joni Mitchell/Ravi Shankar/The Grateful Dead

3

4

5

3: Dido/Jamelia/Madonna/Joss Stone
4: Robbie Williams/Jason Donovan/Nick Cave/Jake Shears
5: The Proclaimers/Bros/The Corrs/B*Witched

Round
12

6

7

6: The Pogues/The Boomtown Rats/The Doors/Public Image Ltd
7: The Streets/Jamelia/Embrace/Beverley Knight

8: Elvis Costello/Kate Bush/Dusty Springfield/Bob Dylan
9: George Harrison/Ritchie Valens/Michael Bolton/Johnny Cash
10: Bob The Builder/Noddy/Chef (South Park)/Mr. Blobby

Round 12

Odd One Out

11

12

11: Peter Gabriel/Elton John/Rod Stewart/Eric Clapton
12: Keanu Reeves/Minnie Driver/Robert Downy Jnr/William Shatner

13
14

15

13: Ian Dury/Sting/Bryan Ferry/Ozzy Osbourne
14: Prince/Bono/Nick Cave/Bob Dylan
15: Ray Davies/Dave Gilmour/David Bowie/Eric Clapton

16

17

16: Ian Brown/George Michael/Chuck Berry/Frank Zappa
17: The Who/Donovan/Joe Cocker/Led Zeppelin

18

19

20

18: Phil Lynot/Flea/Paul McCartney/Sting
19: Kurt Cobain/Sid Vicious/Paul McCartney/Pete Doherty
20: Duncan James /Bryan McFadden/Geri Halliwell/Kerry Katona (Atomic Kitten)

Round 12

Answers

1

Artists shown: ABBA/Rod Stewart/Queen/Cliff Richard
Cliff Richard. All the others have had West End musicals themed around their music, *Mamma Mia, Tonight's The Night* and *We Will Rock You* respectively. Cliff Richard however, has performed in a West End musical, playing the part of Heathcliff in *Wuthering Heights*.

2

Artists shown: Janis Joplin/Joni Mitchell/Ravi Shankar/The Grateful Dead
Joni Mitchell. The other three performed at Woodstock; Joni Mitchell was scheduled to play, but didn't make it. Instead, she did write a hit song 'Woodstock' about the festival.

3

Artists shown: Dido/Jamelia/Madonna/Joss Stone
Madonna. All the others sang a line in Band Aid 20's 'Do They Know It's Christmas'.

4

Artists shown: Robbie Williams/Jason Donovan/Nick Cave/Jake Shears
Jake Shears. They have all duetted with Kylie Minogue, apart from Jake Shears who co-wrote 'I Believe In You' for her.

5

Artists shown: The Proclaimers/Bros/The Corrs/B*Witched
The Corrs. All bands contain family members, but The Corrs are the only group not to include a set of identical twins.

6

Artists shown: The Pogues/The Boomtown Rats/The Doors/Public Image Ltd
The Pogues. All the other bands took their names from novels, The Boomtown Rats from Woody Guthrie's *Bound For Glory*, The Doors from *The Doors Of Perception* by Aldous Huxley, and Public Image Ltd from Muriel Sparks' novel *The Public Image*. The Pogues however, is taken from Gaelic "Pogue mahone" which means "kiss my arse".

7

Artists shown: The Streets/Jamelia/Embrace/Beverley Knight
The Streets. Chris Martin (Coldplay) has written songs for Jamelia ('See It In A Boy's Eyes'), Embrace ('Gravity'), and Beverley Knight ('First Time'). Originally Martin sang on 'Dry Your Eyes' by The Streets, but later asked to pull his vocals from the final mix.

8

Artists shown: Elvis Costello/Kate Bush/Dusty Springfield/Bob Dylan
Kate Bush. All the others have changed their original birth names for the sake of stardom. Originally they were called Declan McManus, Mary O'Brien and Robert Zimmerman respectively.

9

Artists shown: George Harrison/Ritchie Valens/Michael Bolton/Johnny Cash
Ritchie Valens. All the other artists have been successfully sued for plagiarism. George Harrison due to similarities between 'He's So Fine' (The Chiffons) and his own, 'My Sweet Lord', Michael Bolton for similarities between his song 'Love Is A Wonderful Thing' and 'Harvest For The World' by The Isley Brothers, and Johnny Cash was sued by Gordon Jenkins because of the likeness between Jenkins' 'Crescent City Blues' and Cash's 'Folsom Prison Blues'. Ritchie Valens had a massive hit with 'La Bamba' which can be traced back to the 14th Century.

10

Artists shown: Bob The Builder/Noddy/Chef (South Park)/Mr Blobby
Noddy. Bob The Builder, Chef and Mr. Blobby have all had number 1 singles with 'Can We Fix It' (2000), 'Chocolate Salty Balls (P.S. I Love You)' (1998) and 'Mr Blobby' (1993). Poor Noddy's single 'Make Way For Noddy' only made it to number 29 in 2003.

11 Artists shown: Peter Gabriel/Elton John/Rod Stewart/Eric Clapton
Elton John. All the others have had massive solo careers since early success in the bands Genesis, The Faces and The Yardbirds respectively. Elton John didn't start his career as part of a successful band.

12 Artists shown: Keanu Reeves/Minnie Driver/Robert Downy Jnr/William Shatner
Keanu Reeves. They have all released solo albums, apart from Keanu Reeves, who plays bass in a band called Dogstar.

13 Artists shown: Ian Dury/Sting/Bryan Ferry/Ozzy Osbourne
Ozzy Osbourne. Ian Dury, Sting and Bryan Ferry were all teachers before their fame, while Ozzy worked in an abattoir.

14 Artists shown: Prince/Bono/Nick Cave/Bob Dylan
Bob Dylan. Prince, Bono and Nick Cave have all written the screenplays to films, *Graffiti Bridge* (1990), *Million Dollar Hotel* (2000), and *Ghosts... Of The Civil Dead* (1988) respectively. Bob Dylan has only ever co-written screenplays, *Renaldo & Clara*, with Sam Shepard in 1978, and *Masked And Anonymous* in 2003 with Larry Charles. Nick Cave is writing his second screenplay, *The Proposition* due to be released in 2005.

15 Artists shown: Ray Davies/Dave Gilmour/David Bowie/Eric Clapton
David Bowie. All have received CBEs, apart from David Bowie, who turned his down in 2000.

16 Artists shown: Ian Brown/George Michael/Chuck Berry/Frank Zappa
George Michael. Even though he was arrested for lewd conduct in 1998, he was released on bail. Ian Brown, Chuck Berry and Frank Zappa have all spent time in prison; for aggressive behaviour, violation of the Mann act and making a porn film, respectively.

17 Artists shown: The Who/Donovan/Joe Cocker/Led Zeppelin
Led Zeppelin. Jimmy Page was used as a guest guitarist on 'Can't Explain' (The Who), 'Sunshine Superman' (Donovan) and 'With A Little Help From My Friends' (Joe Cocker), but was the permanent guitarist with Led Zeppelin.

18 Artists shown: Phil Lynott/Flea/Paul McCartney/Sting
Flea. They are all bass players, but Flea is the only one who isn't also the lead singer of the band.

19 Artists shown: Kurt Cobain/Sid Vicious/Paul McCartney/Pete Doherty
Kurt Cobain. The other three have all served prison sentences for various drug related incidents, while Kurt Cobain had drug problems but never served a prison sentence. Sid Vicious was imprisoned for allegedly murdering girlfriend Nancy Spungen after an evening of heavy heroin abuse, Paul McCartney spent ten days in a Japanese prison for possession of marijuana and Pete Doherty was convicted after burgling the flat of Carl Bârat (also of The Libertines) to fuel his drug habit.

20 Artists shown: Duncan James/Bryan McFadden/Geri Halliwell/Kerry Katona (Atomic Kitten) **Duncan James**. All the others were the first to leave their respective boy/girl bands (Westlife, Spice Girls and Atomic Kitten). Duncan is still with boy band Blue.

The 1960s *Part 2*

At whose farm in 1969 was the
Woodstock Music and Art Fair *held?*

What song was **Dusty Springfield**'s
*first hit, and was also the first song
to be played on the BBC's* Top Of
The Pops *on 1st Jan 1964?*

Which group did **The Quarrymen** *turn into?*

Which super-group did **Eric Clapton** *and*
Ginger Baker *form, along with* **Steve Winwood**
and **Ric Grech**, *after leaving* **Cream**?

Why was 'Landing Of The Daleks' by **The Earthlings**
banned by the BBC in 1965?

*Which soon to be classic rock super-group
first played together as backing musicians
for* **Donovan**'s *'Hurdy Gurdy Man'?*

Which American band were originally called
The Pendletones?

*Which song took **Des O'Connor** to the top of the UK charts in 1968?*

8

*Who wrote the songs 'Heat Wave' (**Martha & The Vandellas**), 'Can I Get A Witness' (**Marvin Gaye**), 'Reach Out I'll Be There' (**The Four Tops**) and 'Stop! In The Name Of Love' (**The Supremes**)?*

9

*How did **Pink Floyd** decide on their name?*

10

*What was the name of **Tom Jones**'s first band, with whom he recorded tracks for EMI under producer Joe Meek?*

11

*Whose 1963 debut was a cover version of **Lennon & McCartney**'s 'Love Of The Loved'?*

12

What was the first reggae song to top the UK charts in 1969?

13

*What does the MG stand for in **Booker T. & The MG**'s?*

14

The 1960s Part 2

15 *Which band was formed in 1962 by members of Tottenham Hotspur football team in order to raise money to play a match in Holland?*

16 *Which folk group was originally called the* **Ethnic Shuffle Orchestra**?

17 *For whom was* **Bob Dylan**'s *'Lay Lady Lay' written?*

18 *Who are Terry and Julie from* **The Kinks**' *1967 song 'Waterloo Sunset'?*

19 *Which comedian had a number 1 hit with 'Tears' in 1965?*

20 *What type of company did* **Frank Zappa** *start in 1963?*

21 *Which acoustic duo first performed under the name Tom & Jerry?*

Why did the **Faces** *drop the 'Small' from their name in 1968?*

22

From which James Joyce book did **John Lennon** *take the phrase "Goo goo boo joob" which he used in 'I Am The Walrus'?*

23

The Monkees' *1967 number 2 hit 'Alternate Title' was originally called what?*

24

Which group had a number 13 hit with **Bob Dylan**'s *'Blowin' In The Wind' in 1963?*

25

In October 1963, **Bob Dylan** *appeared on a Broadside/Folkways compilation LP titled* Broadside Ballads Vol. 1 *performing three songs, 'John Brown', 'Only A Hobo' and 'Talking Devil' under what pseudonym?*

26

What is **Barry McGuire**'s *only single release, reaching number 3 in 1965?*

27

What was **Elvis Presley**'s *first number 1 single of the 60s?*

28

29

Which were **The Beach Boys'**
two UK number 1 singles?

30

Whose brother wrote 'Lily The Pink'
as part of the band **Scaffold***?*

31

Which song was first recorded by
Smokey Robinson & The Miracles, *then by*
The Isley Brothers, *then by* **Gladys Knight &**
The Pips, *and then* **Marvin Gaye**, *who took it*
to number 1 in 1969?

32

Who played bass on 'The Long And
*Winding Road' (***The Beatles***)?*

33

Which song, originally by **Buddy**
Holly *did* **The Rolling Stones**
release in 1964?

34

What was the first single by by the **Bee Gees**
to make the UK Top 40 in 1967?

Who is Arnold George Dorsey
better known as?

Who was the bass player
on 'Something In The Air'
by **Thunderclap**
Newman?

Which 60s number 1 hit was heavily
influenced by Bach's 'Air On A G
String', 'Sleepers Awake', and
'When A Man Loves A Woman'
by **Percy Sledge**?

How many UK number 1s did
Frank Sinatra *have in the 60s?*

What was **The Beatles**' *first UK*
number 1 single?

Which song was **The Beatles**' *last*
number one single?

Round 13

Answers

1. Max Yasgur (featured in Joni Mitchell's song 'Woodstock' (from *Ladies Of The Canyon* – "I'm going on down to Yasgur's farm, gonna join in a rock and roll band...")

2. 'I Only Want To Be With You' (reaching number 4 in the UK charts)

3. The Beatles

4. Blind Faith (who recorded only one album, *Blind Faith* in 1969)

5. Because it was thought that a Morse distress signal on the record could be confusing to shipping

6. Led Zeppelin

7. The Beach Boys

8. 'I Pretend'

9. Holland-Dozier-Holland (songwriting legends Brian Holland, Lamont Dozier and Eddie Holland also wrote 'Baby Love', 'Bernadette', 'You Keep Me Hangin' On', 'Standing In The Shadows Of Love', 'Nowhere To Run', 'How Sweet It Is (To Be Loved By You)' and 'You Can't Hurry Love' amongst many others)

10. After bluesmen 'Pink' Anderson, and Floyd Council

11. Tommy Scott & The Senators

12. Cilla Black (in 1962 she was working as a hatcheck girl in the Cavern Club, Liverpool. The Beatles urged Brian Epstein to sign the then Cilla White)

13. 'Israelites' (Desmond Dekker & The Aces)

14. Memphis Group (they consisted of Booker T. Jones on keyboard, Steve Cropper on guitar, Lewis Steinberg on bass (later replaced by Donald "Duck" Dunn) and Al Jackson Jr. on drums. The band were all session musicians at Stax Records' studio in Memphis)

15. The Dave Clark Five

16. Fairport Convention

17. Sara Lownds (his wife at the time, 1969)

18. Terence Stamp and Julie Christie (the song is about their relationship)

19. Ken Dodd

20. A porn movie production company (he was later arrested and jailed for sexual perversion)

21 Simon & Garfunkel

22 When the band formed, all five members stood less than 5 ft 6 in height, but when Rod Stewart and Ronnie Wood joined, the word 'small' became unnecessary

23 *Finnegan's Wake*

24 'Randy Scouse Git' (a phrase the band's Mickey Dolenz picked up from the British TV show *Till Death Us Do Part*)

25 Peter, Paul & Mary

26 Blind Boy Grunt

27 'Eve Of Destruction'

28 'It's Now Or Never (O Sole Mio)' (reaching the top spot in 1960, originally written in 1901 by Giovanni Capurro and E. di Capua)

29 'Good Vibrations' (1966) and 'Do It Again' (1968)

30 Paul McCartney. (His brother Michael, who went under the name of Mike McGear, wrote the song, which reached number 1 in 1968)

31 'I Heard It Through The Grapevine'

32 John Lennon

33 'Not Fade Away'

34 'New York Mining Disaster 1941'

35 Engelbert Humperdink (originally known as Gerry Dorsey)

36 Pete Townshend (The Who)

37 'A Whiter Shade Of Pale' (Procol Harum)

38 Two ('Strangers In The Night' (1966), and 'Somethin' Stupid' with daughter Nancy in 1967. His first number 1 was 'Three Coins In The Fountain' in 1954)

39 'From Me To You' (April 1963. Their previous single 'Please Please Me', although reaching number 1 on the *Melody Maker* and *New Musical Express* charts, peaked at number 2)

40 'The Ballad Of John And Yoko' (June 1969)

Film & TV *Part 2*

1. *Which film starred* **Keith Moon** *playing Uncle Ernie,* **Oliver Reed** *playing Frank Hobbs,* **Tina Turner** *playing 'The Acid Queen' and* **Eric Clapton** *playing the Preacher?*

2. *Who played Earl Piggot in* Short Cuts *(1993)?*

3. *An instrumental version of 'Handbags and Gladrags' provides the theme tune to which BBC comedy series?*

4. *The film* Notting Hill *(1999) provided a hit (the song 'She') for which singer?*

5. *Which film featured* **Beck**'s *cover of the song 'Everybody's Gotta Learn Sometime'?*

6. *In which film does 'Up Where We Belong' by* **Joe Cocker** *and* **Jennifer Warnes** *feature?*

7. *Which band wrote the soundtrack to Sophie Coppola's film* The Virgin Suicides *in 2000?*

8. *For which film did* **Destiny's Child** *record 'Independent Women Part One'?*

Film & TV Part 2

Which film star played **Elvis Presley** *in*
Elvis: The Movie?

9

Which **Urge Overkill** *song was featured on the*
Pulp Fiction *soundtrack?*

10

Which song by **Aqualung** *was featured in the*
Volkswagen Beetle *TV advert in 2002?*

11

Who voices the parts of Dougal and Florence in
the 2005 animated feature of
The Magic Roundabout?

12

Rufus Wainwright *made his*
big screen debut in which
Martin Scorsese film?

13

Kyle MacLachlan played which
famous keyboard player in which 1991 film?

14

Which rock legend makes a guest appearance
in the film Hi-Fidelity?

15

Which **Bob Dylan** *song provided*
the theme to the BBC TV comedy
Absolutely Fabulous?

16

Patrick Swayze sang which song from the
Dirty Dancing *soundtrack, reaching number*
17 in the UK charts?

17

Round 14

Film & TV Part 2

18 *Which singer won an Oscar in 2003 for the song 'Into The West' which is featured in* Lord Of The Rings: Return Of The King?

19 *Who sung the theme tune to* The Cosby Show?

20 *Who directed* **The Beatles**' *film* Yellow Submarine *in 1968?*

21 *After what is the band* **Black Sabbath** *named?*

22 *Who sang 'Profoundly In Love With Pandora', which was used as the theme tune for* The Secret Diary Of Adrian Mole?

23 *Which song by* **The Clash** *was used in a Levi's 501 advert, helping it to become a major hit in 1991?*

24 *Which ex-***Take That** *member won TV's* Celebrity Big Brother *in 2003?*

25 *Who had a UK number 6 hit in 1985 with 'St Elmo's Fire', the theme tune to the film of the same name?*

Film & TV Part 2

*With which special TV guests did **Gareth Gates** record his Red Nose Day number 1 record 'Spirit In The Sky' in 2003?*

26

Which artist has made a film documentary entitled Welcome To My Nightmare?

27

*Who wrote the James Bond song 'Goldeneye', performed by **Tina Turner**?*

28

*Which song by **Paula Cole** is used as the theme tune to teen drama* Dawson's Creek?

29

*'Deeper Underground' by **Jamiroquai** is featured in which film?*

30

*Which **Beatle** was a producer for Monty Python's* Life Of Brian *in 1979?*

31

*Which James Bond song is sampled on 'Millennium' by **Robbie Williams**?*

32

Which singer has had two hit singles with lead songs from the films Fame *and* Flashdance?

33

*What happened in January 1984 when **Michael Jackson** filmed a TV commercial for Pepsi?*

34

35 *For which film did Kajagoogoo's **Limahl** write the theme song (of the same name), giving him a number 4 hit in 1984?*

36 *Which song by **Cliff Richard** was featured in the film* Serious Charge?

37 *Which band wrote the score for the 1977 William Friedkin film* Sorcerer?

38 *In which film did **Sting** star as the character 'Feyd-Rautha' in 1984?*

39 *Who wrote the tune 'The Wizard', which was used as the* Top Of The Pops *theme for a number of years?*

40 *In which film did **Eminem** star in 2002?*

41 *Name the Gregory Peck film referred to throughout **Bob Dylan**'s 'Brownsville Girl'*

42 *Which two songs by **Iggy Pop** are featured in the film* Trainspotting?

43 *Which song released by the cartoon characters **The Simpsons** went to number 1 in January 1991?*

*What was the theme tune
to* Black Beauty *called?*

44

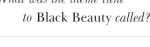

*Which UK number 1 by
LeAnn Rimes was also the theme
tune to the film* Coyote Ugly?

45

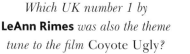

Who has played the characters Milo in Dudes
(1987), Budd in My Own Private Idaho
(1991) and Bob Summerfield in
Psycho *(1998)?*

46

*Which actor played the **Spice Girls**' manager in
the film* Spice World?

47

*Actor Jack Black is also the lead singer
in which band?*

48

*'Mad World' by **Gary Jules** and
Michael Andrews was the UK Christmas
number 1 in 2003. In which film
did it feature?*

49

What was the title song to the Bond film
The Spy Who Loved Me, *and
who performed it?*

50

*Which artist has recorded 'Not Of This Earth'
and 'Misunderstood', featured in the two*
Bridget Jones *films?*

51

1	*Tommy* (1975, written by Pete Townshend (The Who) and Ken Russell. The film also starred Elton John playing Tommy)
2	Tom Waits
3	*The Office* (originally a hit for Chris Farlowe in 1967 and Stereophonics in 2001)
4	Elvis Costello ('She' reached number 19 in the UK charts that year)
5	*Eternal Sunshine Of The Spotless Mind*
6	*An Officer And A Gentleman*
7	Air
8	*Charlie's Angels*
9	Kurt Russell
10	'Girl You'll Be A Woman Soon' (originally a hit for Neil Diamond)
11	'Strange And Beautiful (I'll Put A Spell On You)'
12	Robbie Williams and Kylie Minogue (they also collaborated on the single 'Kids' in 2000)
13	*The Aviator* (2005)
14	Ray Manzarek – *The Doors*
15	Bruce Springsteen (playing himself)
16	'This Wheel's On Fire' (sung by Adrian Edmondson and Jennifer Saunders and originally a number 5 hit in 1968 for Julie Driscoll, Brian Auger and The Trinity)
17	'She's Like The Wind'
18	Annie Lennox
19	Bobby McFerrin
20	George Dunning
21	A 1963 Boris Karloff horror film
22	Ian Dury And The Blockheads
23	'Should I Stay Or Should I Go'
24	Mark Owen (on the back of the programme Owen scored two top 20 hit singles, and created his own record label, Sedna)
25	John Parr

26 The Kumars (originally a hit for Norman Greenbaum in 1970, and Doctor And The Medics in 1986)

27 Alice Cooper

28 Bono & The Edge

29 'I Don't Want To Wait'

30 *Godzilla*

31 George Harrison

32 'You Only Live Twice'

33 Irene Cara

34 His hair caught fire and he was taken to hospital for serious burn injuries, causing yet more speculation about his plastic surgery

35 *The Never Ending Story*

36 'Living Doll' (which reached number 1 in 1959)

37 Tangerine Dream

38 *Dune*

39 Paul Hardcastle

40 *Eight Mile*

41 *The Gunfighter* (1950)

42 'Lust For Life' and 'Nightclubbing'

43 'Do The Bartman'

44 'Galloping Home' (1974)

45 'Can't Fight The Moonlight'

46 Flea (Red Hot Chili Peppers – real name Michael Balzary)

47 Richard E. Grant

48 Tenacious D

49 *Donnie Darko* (2001)

50 'Nobody Does It Better' – Carly Simon

51 Robbie Williams

The 1970s *Part 2*

1   *What was the first rap record to become a hit?*

2   *Which 70s band is made up of a Cowboy, Indian, GI, Policeman and Construction Worker?*

3   *From which novel did the* **Boomtown Rats** *get their name?*

4   *Who had an accidental hit with 'Kung Fu Fighting' in 1974?*

5   *What is* **Joni Mitchell**'s *only UK top 20 single ?*

6   *Which Lou Reed song has* **David Bowie** *covered?*

7   *Which song has been* **The Eagles**' *only UK top 10 hit, reaching number 8 in 1977?*

8   *Who played the kazoo on* **Ringo Starr**'s *'You're Sixteen' in 1974?*

*What was the name of **Keith Moon**'s first solo album, released in 1975?*

9

*What do **Neil Young**'s 1972 album* Harvest *and **Meat Loaf**'s 1978 album* Bat Out Of Hell *have in common?*

10

*Which 70s rock band was formed from members of **Free**, **Mott The Hoople** and **King Crimson**?*

11

Which famous guitarist's guitar is made from an 1870 mahogany fireplace, a bike saddle, a knitting needle and valve springs from a motorbike engine?

12

*What was the last song that **Elvis Presley** performed live?*

13

*Which country banned **Pink Floyd**'s 'Another Brick In The Wall'?*

14

*Which hit single by The Osmonds did **Boyzone** take to number 2 in the charts in 1994?*

15

16

Both **Harold Melvin and the Bluenotes**,
and **Thelma Houston** *released a version
of which song in 1977?*

17

Why was **Paul Simon***'s
'Kodachrome' banned from airplay
by the BBC?*

18

Which band comprising **Howard Devoto**,
Pete Shelley, **Steve Diggle** *and* **John Maher**
formed after witnessing an early
Sex Pistols *concert?*

19

Which **Michael Jackson** *number 7 hit, was
originally recorded by* **Bill Withers** *in 1972?*

20

Who was a founding member of **The Electric
Light Orchestra** *along with Jeff Lyne, but left
after the first album due to musical differences,
and founded* **Wizzard***?*

21

How many number 1s did **Slade** *have,
all of which were between October 1971
and December 1973?*

Which country singer is featured on
Bob Dylan'*s* Desire?

22

Which was the first **Genesis** *hit to feature*
Phil Collins on lead vocals?

23

Which rock band did
David Coverdale assemble
after leaving **Deep Purple**
in 1976?

24

Who replaced Syd Barrett as
lead singer of **Pink Floyd**?

25

Whose songs were featured extensively
throughout Robert Altman's 1971 film
McCabe And Mrs Miller, *starring Warren*
Beatty and Julie Christie?

26

Which double-A-side record took
David Cassidy *to the top of the*
charts for the second time in 1973?

27

What item of clothing did the original copies of
Alice Cooper'*s 'School's Out' come with?*

28

29

In the early hours of April 29th, 1976, who famously climbed over the wall at **Elvis Presley**'s Graceland home and tried to knock on the front door after noticing a light was on?

30

Name **Steely Dan**'s only UK Top 10 album?

31

With which song did **Rod Stewart** have his first UK number 1 hit?

32

Which band has gone under the pseudonyms Dukes Of The Stratosphere, The Young Ones, Too Many Cooks and Three Wise Men?

33

Which song was allegedly written one moonlit night, when the artist did her "witch impression"?

34

For which DJ's radio show was **Joy Division**'s 'Love Will Tear Us Apart' first recorded?

Whose box-set Fruit Tree *was released
posthumously in 1979?*

35

Which 70s band formed from initially being
Linda Ronstadt's *backing group on her*
Silk Purse *album?*

36

Which **Paul McCartney & Wings** *album cover
features Michael Parkinson, Clement Freud and
Christopher Lee amongst others?*

37

*What was the first single to be released
on the* **Rolling Stones**' *own label,
Rolling Stones Records?*

38

What name did **Hawkwind**
change to in the late 70s?

39

*Which seventies band is named after a 1966
William Manus novel?*

40

Round
15

Answers

1   'Rapper's Delight' (Sugarhill Gang, reaching number 3 in 1979, the single was based on 'Good Times' by Chic)

2   The Village People

3   *Bound For Glory* by Woody Guthrie

4   Carl Douglas (the song was originally intended as the B-side to 'I Want To Give You My Everything' and was recorded in just 15 minutes)

5   'Big Yellow Taxi' (number 11, 1970)

6   'White Light White Heat' (only live versions are available. Bowie played this song on two 1972 BBC radio sessions. The song was also recorded for the covers album *Pin-Up's* but never released)

7   'Hotel California'

8   Paul McCartney

9   *Two Sides Of The Moon*

10   Apart from the fact that they are each artists' biggest selling albums, both records spawned hugely successful sequels in the 1990s, Young's *Harvest Moon* in 1992 and Meat Loaf's *Back Out Of Hell II: Back Into Hell* a year later

11   Bad Company

12   Brian May's (Queen) Red Special

13   'Bridge Over Troubled Water' (Indianapolis, June 1977)

14   South Africa (in Soweto, a South African town, thousands of black children chanted this song during a student strike against apartheid, while conflicting with the police across the barricades)

15   'Love Me For A Reason' (a number 1 for The Osmonds in 1974)

16   'Don't Leave Me This Way' (the original being by Harold Melvin and the Bluenotes, and later covered again in 1986 by The Communards with Sarah Jane Morris)

17   Because it contained a product brand-name

18   The Buzzcocks

19   'Ain't No Sunshine'

20   Roy Wood

Answers

21 Six ('Coz I Love You', 'Take Me Bak 'Ome', 'Mama Weer All Crazee Now', 'Cum On Feel The Noize', 'Skweeze Me, Pleeze Me')

22 Emmylou Harris

23 'Follow You, Follow Me' (1978)

24 Whitesnake

25 Dave Gilmour (Barrett was sacked for erratic behaviour)

26 Leonard Cohen (the songs were 'Winter Lady', 'The Stranger Song' and 'Sisters Of Mercy', tracks 3, 4 and 5 respectively from his debut album *Songs Of Leonard Cohen*)

27 'Daydreamer/The Puppy Song' (his first number 1 was in 1972 with 'How Can I Be Sure')

28 Disposable paper panties

29 Bruce Springsteen (who had played a show earlier that night in Memphis. A security guard interceded before he could knock, telling him that Elvis had left the building as he was in Lake Tahoe at the time)

30 *'Aja'*, (which reached number 5 in 1977)

31 'Maggie May/Reason To Believe' (1971)

32 XTC

33 'Wuthering Heights' (Kate Bush number 1 in 1978)

34 John Peel (in December 1979)

35 Nick Drake

36 The Eagles

37 *Band On The Run*

38 'Brown Sugar' (April 1971)

39 Hawklord (after science fiction authors Michael Moorcock and Michael Butterworth featured the group in their 1976 novel *The Time Of The Hawklords*)

40 Mott The Hoople (book of the same name)

Opening Songs

Name the opening tracks on these classic albums:

1
Jeff Buckley – Grace

2
R.E.M. – Automatic For The People

3
Bon Jovi – Slippery When Wet

4
Oasis – (What's The Story)
Morning Glory?

5
Bob Dylan – Blonde On Blonde

6
Fleetwood Mac – Rumours

7
U2 – Achtung Baby

8
Air – Moon Safari

David Bowie – Low

9

Pink Floyd – The Wall

10

Neil Young – Rust Never Sleeps

11

Van Morrison – Moondance

12

Elton John –
Goodbye Yellow Brick Road

13

Pulp – Different Class

14

Bruce Springsteen – Tunnel Of Love

15

The Sex Pistols –
Never Mind The Bollocks

16

Round
16

17
Sly & The Family Stone –
There's A Riot Goin' On

18
Public Enemy – It Takes A Nation Of
Millions To Hold Us Back

19
Red Hot Chili Peppers –
BloodSugarSexMagik

20
Talking Heads –
Remain In Light

21
Coldplay – A Rush Of Blood To The Head

22
Blondie – Parallel Lines

23
Kate Bush – Hounds Of Love

24
Moby – Play

Radiohead – OK Computer

25

Damien Rice – O

26

Michael Jackson – Thriller

27

The Killers – Hot Fuss

28

Joni Mitchell – Blue

29

The Beatles – Revolver

30

Lou Reed – Transformer

31

The Police – Ghost In The Machine

32

The Smiths – Meat Is Murder

33

34   **The Cure** – Seventeen Seconds

35   **Nirvana** – In Utero

36   **Madonna** – Ray Of Light

37   **The Rolling Stones** – Exile On Main St.

38   **Carole King** – Tapestry

39   **Iron Maiden** – The Number Of The Beast

40   **The Clash** – The Clash

41   **The Doors** – L.A. Woman

42   **INXS** – Kick

ABBA – Arrival

Stevie Wonder –
Songs In The Key Of Life

Bob Marley – Exodus

Dire Straits – Brothers In Arms

Led Zeppelin – Led Zeppelin II

Joy Division – Closer

Queen – A Kind Of Magic

Franz Ferdinand – Franz Ferdinand

1 'Mojo Pin'

2 'Drive'

3 'Let It Rock'

4 'Hello'

5 'Rainy Day Women #12 & #35'

6 'Second Hand News'

7 'Zoo Station'

8 'La Femme D'Argent'

9 'Speed Of Life'

10 'In The Flesh?'

11 'My My, Hey Hey, (Out Of The Blue)'

12 'And It Stoned Me'

13 'Funeral For A Friend/Love Lies Bleeding'

14 'Mis-Shapes'

15 'Ain't Got You'

16 'Holidays In The Sun'

17 'Luv N' Haight'

18 'Countdown To Armageddon'

19 'The Power Of Equality'

20 'Born Under Punches (The Heat Goes On)'

21 'Politik'

22 'Hanging On The Telephone'

23 'Running Up That Hill (A Deal With God)'

24 'Honey'

25 'Airbag'

26   'Delicate'

27   'Wanna Be Startin' Somethin''

28   'Jenny Was A Friend Of Mine'

29   'All I Want'

30   'Taxman'

31   'Vicious'

32   'Spirits In The Material World'

33   'Headmaster Ritual'

34   'Reflection'

35   'Serve The Servants'

36   'Drowned World/Substitute For Love'

37   'Rocks Off'

38   'I Feel The Earth Move'

39   'Invaders'

40   'Janie Jones'

41   'Changeling'

42   'Guns In The Sky'

43   'When I Kissed The Teacher'

44   'Love's In Need Of Love Today'

45   'Natural Mystic'

46   'So Far Away'

47   'Whole Lotta Love'

48   'Heart And Soul'

49   'Princes Of The Universe'

50   'Jacqueline'

The 1980s *Part 2*

1. *Which **Olivia Newton-John** song was the biggest selling US single in the 80s?*

2. *In which year did **Band Aid** first record 'Do They Know It's Christmas'?*

3. *Which was the first British punk band to record, chart and tour in America?*

4. *Which singer was the first British female artist to top the UK album charts?*

5. *Which **Clannad** album was inspired by the TV show Robin Of Sherwood?*

6. *Slices of which fruit are featured on the cover of **The Stone Roses** album The Stone Roses?*

7

*Which 80s pop one hit wonder, had a number 2 hit with 'Mickey' in 1982, and also directed the video for 'Once In A Lifetime' by **Talking Heads**?*

8

*Which band was **Belinda Carlisle** in before her solo career took off?*

9

*Which UK duo did Johnny Marr and Bernard Sumner create after leaving **The Smiths** and **New Order** respectively?*

10

Who had a number 1 hit with 'Doctorin' The Tardis' in 1988?

11

*About which 80s 'Hair Metal' rocker was **Aerosmith**'s 'Dude (Looks Like A Lady)' supposedly written?*

12

*With whom did **Elaine Paige** duet on the number 1 single 'I Know Him So Well'?*

13

*To whom is **U2**'s 'Pride (In The Name Of Love)' a tribute?*

Round
17

The 1980s Part 2

14
*For which band's debut album did **All About Eve**'s Julian Regan sing backing vocals?*

15
Which band did teenagers Susanne Sulley and Joanne Catherall join in 1980, after being spotted at a nightclub?

16
*What was **Michael Jackson**'s first UK number 1 single as a solo artist?*

17
Which 1986 album features the songs 'Trendy Kinnock', 'Andy And Fergie', 'Uranus', 'I've Never Met A Nice South African' and 'We're Scared Of Bob'?

18
*Which musical contains the song 'I Am What I Am' which was a huge hit for **Gloria Gaynor** in 1984?*

19
*Which heavy metal band did Bruce Dickinson leave to join **Iron Maiden**?*

20
*What has been **Boris Gardiner**'s only UK number 1 single?*

The 1980s Part 2

*The line "A jumped up pantry boy,
who never knew his place" from*
The Smiths *'This Charming Man',
is taken from which 1972 film?*

21

Who wrote all the songs for **Jennifer Warnes'**
1987 Famous Blue Raincoat *album?*

22

*Which single did 'Wicksy' (Nick Berry) from
EastEnders release, which topped the charts,
and was one of the best selling singles of 1986?*

23

What does **LL Cool J** *stand for?*

24

*From which album do the songs 'Could You
Be Loved', and 'Redemption Song' come?*

25

*Who played the harmonica on 'There Must
Be An Angel (Playing With My Heart)'
by the* **Eurythmics** *and 'I Feel For You'
by* **Chaka Khan**?

26

What reason did **Prince** *give for
cancelling his two Wembley gigs in
London in July 1987?*

27

28 *Which MP appeared in the video to 'My Guy' by* **Tracey Ullman***?*

29 *Who penned* **Barbra Streisand***'s only UK number 1 single 'Woman In Love'?*

30 *Which* **Tina Turner** *single was written by* **Mark Knopfler***, and features* **Jeff Beck** *on guitar?*

31 *Who released an album in 1981 called* Nah=Poo – The Art Of Bluff?

32 **The Thompson Twins** *are named after characters from which comic storybooks?*

33 *Who released '99 Red Balloons', a number 1 hit in 1984?*

34 *Which band was the first Western group to play in China?*

*How did **Def Leppard** drummer **Rick Allen** lose an arm?*

35

Who had a number 1 single with 'You'll Never Stop Me Loving You' in 1989?

36

*Which song did actor **Bruce Willis** record and release in 1987?*

37

*Which band is made up of **Graham McPherson**, **Mike Benson**, **Chris Foreman**, **Mark Bedford**, **Cathal Smyth**, **Lee Thompson** and **Daniel Woodgate**?*

38

*The singers of which band left to form **Fun Boy Three**?*

39

*Which comedian featured in **Shakin' Stevens**'s video for 'What Do You Want To Make Those Eyes At Me For'?*

40

1 'Physical' (making it to number 7 in the UK in 1981)

2 November 1984

3 The Damned

4 Kate Bush (with *Never Forever* in 1980)

5 *Legend* (1984)

6 Lemon

7 Toni Basil

8 The Go Go's (this was the first all female band to have a number 1 single, 'We Got The Beat', and album *Beauty And The Beat* simultaneously in the US charts)

9 Electronic

10 The Timelords (who also wrote the successful book, *The Manual (How To Have A Number One – The Easy Way)*

11 Vince Neil from Mötley Crüe (meeting Vince inspired the band to write the song)

12 Barbara Dickson (from the musical *Chess*)

13 Martin Luther King

14 The Mission (*God's Own Medicine* in 1986. The Mission's lead singer Wayne Hussey co-produced the All About Eve single 'Our Summer')

15 The Human League

16 'One Day In Your Life' (1981, from his album *Forever Michael*)

17 *Spit In Your Ear* (Spitting Image)

18 *La Cage Aux Folles* (by Jerry Herman)

19 Samson (he replaced the original Iron Maiden singer Paul Di'Anno in 1981)

20 'I Wanna Wake Up With You' (1986)

21 *Sleuth* (a hit for The Smiths in 1983)

22 Leonard Cohen (Warnes is a long-time backing singer for Cohen)

23 'Every Loser Wins'

24 Ladies Love Cool James

25 *Uprising* by Bob Marley & The Wailers (1980)

26 Stevie Wonder

27 "Bad weather"

28 Neil Kinnock

29 Barry Gibb

30 'Private Dancer'

31 Wah!

32 *Tintin*

33 Nena (a one hit wonder in the UK, although Nena had greater chart success in her native Germany with 13 hits)

34 Wham! (in 1985)

35 He was in a car crash in Yorkshire in December 1984. (Allen continues to play the drums for the band by using specially-developed foot pedals)

36 Sonia

37 'Under The Boardwalk' (charting at number 2)

38 Madness (otherwise known as Suggs, Mike, Chris, Bedders, Chas Smash, Lee and Woody)

39 The Specials

40 Vic Reeves

Pop Trivia *Part 4*

1 *What is the biggest selling 12 inch single of all time?*

2 *How tall is **Prince**?*

3 *Who has scored the most number 1 singles in the US?*

4 *How many singles were released from **Michael Jackson**'s album Thriller?*

5 *Who was the first black singer to have a British number 1?*

6 *For which song did **Coldplay** win the Best Record award at the 2003 Grammys?*

7 *Two acts share the top spot for having the most number 1 singles, who are they?*

8 *Which UK duo scored an embarrassing 'nul points' in 2003's Eurovision song contest?*

9 *The creators of Wallace & Gromit (Steven R Johnson, Brothers Quay and Nick Park) also did the animation for which **Peter Gabriel** song?*

*In which band is **Flea** the bass player?*

10

*What was **Elton John**'s first solo UK number 1 single?*

11

Which was the first band to be signed to Richard Branson's V2 records?

12

Who started the Motown record label in 1957?

13

*In which country was **Nick Drake** born?*

14

Who had hits with 'Cowpunchers Cantata', 'Meet Me On The Corner' and 'Gilly Gilly Ossenfeffer Katzenellenbogen By The Sea'?

15

When was the BBC's Top Of The Pops *first broadcast?*

16

*Who was **Sting**'s 'An Englishman In New York' written about?*

17

Round 18

18 *Whose real name is James Jewel Osterberg?*

19 *Which artist is hidden in this anagram?*
AN ACUTE GIRLISH AIR

20 *Which film did* **Rod Stewart** *direct in 1999?*

21 *What was the first UK number 1 single by an Irish band?*

22 *Which artist is also known as 'The Boss'?*

23 *Which two figures inspired* **Marilyn Manson**'s *name?*

24 *Which rocker wrote the comic-novel* The Adventures Of Lord Iffy Boatrace?

25 *What are* **Morrissey**'s *two forenames?*

26 *Which* **Beatle** *composed the soundtrack to 1968's* Wonderwall *film?*

Pop Trivia Part 4

Who plays lead guitar on
Joe Cocker's *1968 version of*
'With A Little Help From
My Friends'?

27

Who is the fastest selling rap artist,
and with what album?

28

What are the names of
Liam Gallagher's *two sons?*

29

What is the name of **Michael Jackson**'s
2,700 acre Californian ranch?

30

Who released the singles 'Eat It' and 'Smells
Like Nirvana', parodies of 'Beat It' and 'Smells
Like Teen Spirit' respectively?

31

Who provided backing vocals on **U2**'s
'Pride (In The Name Of Love)'?

32

Which song has topped the UK
singles charts a record five times, and by which
four different artists?

33

How old was **Jerry Lee Lewis**'s *wife Myra*
when he married her?

34

35 Who has released albums entitled
Swordfishtrombones *(1983)*,
Bone Machine *(1992)* and
Mule Variations *(1999)*?

36 Which soul singer is the daughter
of **Nat "King" Cole**?

37 In which year did MTV first go on air?

38 What was the first hit by a UK artist to top the
US charts without entering the British charts?

39 Under what name did
Sonny & Cher first perform?

40 Which band was originally called
On A Friday?

41 What does rap crew **N.W.A.** stand for?

42 Who is the sister of **Billy J. Kramer**?

43 Where was **Cliff Richard** born?

Pop Trivia Part 4

*Who played lead guitar on 'On Broadway' (**The Drifters**), piano on 'Love' (**John Lennon**), sang backing vocals on 'My Sweet Lord' (**George Harrison**) and played maracas on **The Rolling Stones**' 'Not Fade Away'?*

44

*Who sang the opening line in **Band Aid 20**'s version of 'Do They Know It's Christmas?'*

45

*Which song by **The Doors** is featured in the 1987 film The Lost Boys?*

46

*Which song by **Panjabi MC** samples the Knightrider theme?*

47

*Who sings the vocals on **Massive Attack**'s 'Teardrop'?*

48

*Which four stars were in the **Million Dollar Quartet**?*

49

*To whom can **Moby** trace his ancestry back?*

50

Round

18

1   'Blue Monday' by New Order (1983)

2   Five foot two

3   Bing Crosby (with 38 hits)

4   Six ('The Girl Is Mine' (with Paul McCartney), 'Billie Jean', 'Beat It', 'Wanna Be Startin' Somethin'','Thriller' and 'P.Y.T. (Pretty Young Thing)')

5   Harry Belafonte with 'Mary's Boy Child' (1957)

6   'Clocks'

7   The Beatles and Elvis Presley (both acts have had 17 number 1s)

8   Jemini – 'Cry Baby'

9   'Sledgehammer' (1986)

10 Red Hot Chili Peppers

11 'Sacrifice' (1990) (he scored a number 1 hit in 1976 with Kiki Dee 'Don't Go Breaking My Heart')

12 Stereophonics (in 1996)

13 Berry Gordy (songwriter Gordy had his first taste of chart success with Jackie Wilson's 'Reet Petite')

14 Burma (he moved with his parents to Tamworth-In-Arden, nr. Coventry, England when he was six)

15 Max Bygraves

16 New Year's Day 1964 (it was originally conceived as a rival to ITV's Ready Steady Go)

17 Quentin Crisp

18 Iggy Pop

19 CHRISTINA AGUILERA

20 Heel Against The Head

21 'Rat Trap' (The Boomtown Rats, 1978)

22 Bruce Springsteen

23 Marilyn Monroe and Charles Manson (all the members of the band are named after model first name, and a serial killer last name)

24 Bruce Dickinson (he also wrote a second novel in 1993 *The Missionary Position*)

25 Stephen Patrick

26 George Harrison

27 Jimmy Page

28 Eminem with *The Marshall Mathers EP* (which sold 1.76 million albums in the first week of release)

29 Lennon and Gene

30 Neverland

31 "Weird Al" Yankovic

32 Chrissie Hynde

33 'Unchained Melody' – Jimmy Young (1955 for three weeks), The Righteous Brothers (1965 for two weeks, and again for four weeks in 1990), Robson & Jerome (for seven weeks in 1995), and Gareth Gates (four weeks in 2002)

34 12 years old (in the US, each state even now, has its own laws about the lowest age at which a child can marry)

35 Tom Waits

36 Natalie Cole

37 1981 (August)

38 'To Sir With Love', Lulu (1967) (Lulu was just 19 when she recorded the single, which was also the title theme from the movie in which she co-starred with Sidney Poitier)

39 Caesar & Cleo

40 Radiohead

41 Niggaz With Attitude

42 Elkie Brooks

43 India

44 Phil Spector

45 Chris Martin (Coldplay)

46 'People Are Strange' (cover version by Echo And The Bunnymen)

47 'Mundian To Bach Ke'

48 Elizabeth Fraser (Cocteau Twins)

49 Jerry Lee Lewis, Carl Perkins, Elvis Presley and Johnny Cash

50 The author of *Moby Dick* (Herman Meville)

Deaths

1 *Who replaced **Bon Scott** as lead singer of **AC/DC** after the former died?*

2 *A 16 year-old **Dave Dee** was working as a police cadet and was called to the scene of which American rock legend's fatal car crash?*

3 *What killed **Bob Marley**?*

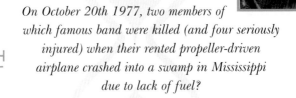

4 *On October 20th 1977, two members of which famous band were killed (and four seriously injured) when their rented propeller-driven airplane crashed into a swamp in Mississippi due to lack of fuel?*

5 *Which rap artist was killed during a drive-by shooting on September 7th 1996?*

6 *Which rapper was killed in a drive-by shooting the following year in March 1997?*

7 *How old was **Sid Vicious** (real name, John Simon Ritchie) when he died of a heroin overdose?*

Which singer-songwriter died in December 2000 after being hit by a speedboat off the coast of Mexico?

8

Where was **The Rolling Stones'** **Brian Jones** *found at the time of his death in 1969?*

9

Which celebrated white blues singer died at the age of 27 in her room at the Landmark Hotel, Los Angeles, October 1970?

10

In which year did **INXS** *front-man* **Michael Hutchence** *die?*

11

What sport was **"Sonny" Bono** *doing which caused his death?*

12

Which singer-songwriter jumped into the Mississippi at Memphis Harbour for an evening swim, was swept under by a wave and drowned?

13

How did **Fairport Convention** *singer* **Sandy Denny** *die in 1978?*

14

Deaths

15

*In which year did **Beatles**
manager **Brian Epstein**
die at the age of 32?*

16

*Who shot **Marvin Gaye** dead in April 1984?*

17

*In which year did jazz legend
Miles Davis die?*

18

*Who went to Cambridge University in 1968,
released his debut album in 1969 with members
of **Fairport Convention** as session musicians,
released a follow up in 1970 with session
musicians such as **John Cale** and **Richard
Thompson**, refused to give press interviews,
and refused to perform live at all after 1970?*

19

*Who was driving the car that crashed
killing **Marc Bolan** instantly in 1977?*

20

*Who died along with **Ritchie Valens** and
The Big Bopper at the edge of a cornfield in
Clear Lake, Iowa?*

In which area of London was
Jimi Hendrix *found dead, in a*
basement bedroom at the
Samarkand Hotel?

21

Which singer was said to have died choking on
a ham sandwich, although in reality she died of
a massive heart attack?

22

Which drummer died in the same apartment
as **Mama Cass Elliot** *had died in,*
four years later?

23

How did **Led Zeppelin** *drummer*
John Bonham *die?*

24

Which famous guitarist died in a helicopter
crash in August 1990?

25

Which gangster rapper launched
Ruthless Records in 1985, co-founded rap
group **N.W.A.** *in 1988, released his own debut*
album in 1989, and died of AIDS in 1995?

26

27 *What was special about the plane that **John Denver** was travelling in when it crashed in 1997?*

28 *How old was **Nat "King" Cole** when he died?*

29 *From which song did **Kurt Cobain** quote in his suicide note?*

30 *Who was working on his sixth album From A Basement On A Hill, when he committed suicide in 2003?*

31 *Who played the character of **Ray Charles** in the 2004 film Ray?*

32 *What was **Freddie Mercury**'s final album with **Queen** before he died in 1991?*

33 *The bassist from which of Britain's most successful bands died in Las Vegas on 28th June 2002 aged 57?*

34 *In which year did **Ian Curtis** of **Joy Division** commit suicide?*

Which song by **Nine Inch Nails** *did* **Johnny Cash** *release in 2003, shortly before his death?*

35

Which member of R&B group **TLC** *was killed in a car accident in Honduras in 2002?*

36

What book was Mark Chapman reading at the scene just after he shot **John Lennon** *seven times?*

37

Which artist was appointed Czechoslovakia's Cultural Liaison Officer in 1991, and also around that time announced his intention of standing as an independent candidate in the US Presidential election?

38

In which room was **Jim Morrison** *found dead in Paris, 1971?*

39

Which artist recorded over 50 albums, married **George Jones** *in 1969, and collaborated on 'Justified & Ancient' with the* **KLF** *in 1992?*

40

1   Brian Johnson (Scott died from suffocating on his own vomit after a heavy night of drink and drug abuse)

2   Eddie Cochran (who was killed on April 17th 1960 when the taxi in which he was traveling en route to London crashed into a lamppost on the A4, throwing him head first through the windshield (his girlfriend Sharon Sheeley, fellow rocker Gene Vincent, tour manager Pat Thomkins and cab driver George Martin all survived the accident). Dee salvaged Cochran's Gretsch guitar from the road and would sometimes play it at the police station, before returning it to Cochran's mother two months later)

3   A brain tumour (at the age of 36)

4   Lynyrd Skynyrd (singer Ronnie Van Zant and guitarist Steve Gaines, as well as four other passengers, were killed)

5   Tupac Shakur (to date no one has been arrested in connection to the killing, though it is thought to be gang related. Thanks to his mother, Tupac's records have made more money now than when he was alive)

6   Notorious BIG (aka Biggie Smalls)

7   21 (Vicious was charged with the murder of girlfriend Nancy Spungen, and apparently preferred death over prison, so begged his mother for a lethal dose of heroin)

8   Kirsty MacColl

9   At the bottom of his swimming pool (the coroners verdict was "death by misadventure" though many people believe he was murdered)

10   Janis Joplin (from a pure batch of heroin. *Pearl*, the album she was recording at the time was released after her death)

11   1997, 22nd November. (The coroners verdict was a suicide hanging due to depression, although as Hutchence was naked many believe his death was the result of an auto eroticism experiment)

12   Skiing (California in 1998, aged 62)

13   Jeff Buckley (aged 31)

14   She fell down a flight of stairs at a friends house, causing her to go into a coma, then died four days later

15   August 1967 (Epstein was found dead in his home from an accidental overdose of sleeping pills, although many believe it was suicide. He was becoming increasingly depressed owing to his growing lack of involvement with The Beatles)

16   His father, a retired minister (Gaye was shot by his father several times in the chest after arguments allegedly after some "insurance dealings")

17   1991 (from pneumonia and a stroke)

18 Nick Drake (who over-dosed on anti-depressants in 1974, after suffering bouts of severe depression since 1972)

19 Gloria Jones (Bolan's common law wife)

20 Buddy Holly (the aeroplane they were travelling in crashed, killing all three of them, and the pilot)

21 Notting Hill Gate (he had overdosed on *quinalbarbitone*, a German barbiturate)

22 'Mama' Cass Elliot (her heart was weakened due to her severe diet, based on one meal a week

23 Keith Moon (1978)

24 He choked to death on his own vomit (after downing 40 measures of vodka)

25 Stevie Ray Vaughn

26 Eazy-E (real name Eric Wright)

27 It was homemade (the craft, a *Long E-Z* had run out of fuel, and dropped into the ocean just off the California coast)

28 45 (born in March 1919, died of lung cancer in February 1965)

29 'Hey Hey, My My (Into The Black)' by Neil Young (Cobain shot himself on April 5th 1993)

30 Elliott Smith (he died from a knife wound to the chest, at the age of 34)

31 Jamie Fox

32 *Innuendo*

33 John Entwistle (from The Who – cause of death: heart attack)

34 1980 (he hanged himself)

35 'Hurt' (the song received critical acclaim, and received the Best Cinematography In A Video award at the 2003 MTV Awards)

36 Lisa 'Left Eye' Lopes (she was 30 years old)

37 *The Catcher In The Rye* by J.D. Salinger (Chapman shouted "I am Holden Caulfield, the catcher in the rye of the present generation" as he was arrested)

38 Frank Zappa (he was diagnosed with cancer, which prevented him from continuing with his candidature. Zappa died in 1993 from prostate cancer)

39 The bathroom (Morrison was found dead in the bath, with the official cause of death as heart failure)

40 Tammy Wynette (she died in 1998 of a blood clot in a lung)

The 1990s *Part 2*

1   *What was the first number 1 single
of the 90s?*

2   *Which 90s band was formed by
ex-***La***'s guitarist **John Power***?*

3   *Which band did **Kim Deal** form
after she left the **Pixies***?*

4   *Which **Paul Weller** album includes the songs 'Broken
Stones', 'Porcelain Gods' and 'Wings Of Speed'?*

5   *Who is the **Manic Street Preachers**'
'Kevin Carter' about?*

6   **Blueboy**'s *'Remember Me'(1997) samples which song?*

7   *Which **Van Morrison** song did **Rod Stewart** cover,
reaching number 5 in 1993?*

8   *Who remixed **Everything But The Girl**'s 'Missing' in
1995, sending to number 3 in the UK charts, and
giving them their biggest hit since 1988?*

*On **k d Lang**'s 1997 album*
Drag, *to what do all the songs
on the album refer?*

9

Which band released albums entitled
Badmotorfinger *(1992)*, Superunknown
(1994) and Down On The Upside *(1996)?*

10

*What does **Korn**'s 'A.D.I.D.A.S.'
single stand for?*

11

*Which football star is shown on the
cover of the **Ash** single 'Kung-Fu'?*

12

*On which **Massive Attack** single
does **Tracey Thorn** sing lead vocals?*

13

*From which album do the songs 'Remember',
'Sexy Boy' and 'You Make It Easy' come?*

14

*Which **Nirvana** song was
inspired by Patrick
Süskind's novel* Perfume?

15

The 1990s Part 2

16 Which former member of 90's band **Bros**, is now the manager of **Pink**?

17 Which animal did **Tori Amos** breast feed for the cover of her Boys For Pele *(1996)* album artwork?

18 Which band staged a paint attack on their old label, FM Revolver, in 1990 causing £23,000 worth of damage?

19 During which song did **Jarvis Cocker** pull a moonie at the 1996 Brit Awards?

20 What was **Geri Halliwell**'s first UK number 1 single after leaving the **Spice Girls**?

21 Which number 1 single by **Spacedust** used a sample from Jane Fonda's Workout record?

Whose first 1993 release was a limited edition mini-album entitled Live At Sine?

22

From which 1993 album do the songs 'Blow Your Mind', 'Didgin' Out' and 'Too Young To Die' come?

23

What is the title of **Shakespeare's Sister**s' *second album, containing the number 1 hit single 'Stay'?*

24

Which band featured in an episode of The Simpsons, *performing their 1994 hit 'Give It Away'?*

25

Tim Burgess *is the lead singer of which 'Madchester' band?*

26

What was the first single to top simultaneously the UK and US singles charts in 1997?

27

28 *What was the name of **Oasis**' debut album, released in 1994?*

29 *Which record label did **Dr. Dre** form in 1991?*

30 *Who was the UK Eurovision entrant in 1993, with her version of 'Better The Devil You Know'?*

31 *Who had a number 3 hit in 1990 with a cover of **The Beatles**' 'Strawberry Fields Forever'?*

32 *Which song is **Prince**'s only UK number 1 hit?*

33 *Who co-wrote **Michael Bolton**'s Steel Bars (1992)?*

34 *In which year was **Radiohead**'s debut album Pablo Honey released?*

Which **Labi Siffre** *song does* **Eminem** *sample in 1999's 'My Name Is'?*

35

*Which ex-***Spice Girl** *was heckled at the V99 festival in 1998 for her rendition of 'Anarchy In The UK'?*

36

Which group released an album in 1990 entitled Efil4zaggin, *which spells 'Niggaz4life' backwards?*

37

Who had a UK number 1 with 'Sweet Like Chocolate' in 1999?

38

Which artist co-wrote 'Justify My Love' with **Madonna***?*

39

The Fugees *had a number 1 hit with a cover of 'Killing Me Softly With His Song' in 1996. Who sang the original in 1973?*

40

Round 20

1   'Hangin' Tough' (New Kids On The Block)

2   Cast

3   The Breeders

4   *Stanley Road* (1995)

5   A photographer friend who committed suicide

6   'Women Of The Ghetto' by Marlena Shaw

7   'Have I Told You Lately'

8   Todd Terry

9   Smoking

10   Soundgarden

11   'All Day I Dream About Sex'

12   Eric Cantona (showing his famous lunge at an abusive Crystal Palace supporter in 1995)

13   'Protection' (1995 – reaching number 14)

14   *Moon Safari* – Air (1998)

15   'Scentless Apprentice' (1993)

16   Craig Logan

17   A piglet

18   The Stone Roses (FM Revolver had made a video to promote the single 'Sally Cinnamon' without the bands approval or permission)

19   'Earth Song' – Michael Jackson

20   'Mi Chico Latino' (1999)

Answers

21   'Gym & Tonic' (1998)

22   Jeff Buckley

23   *Emergency On Planet Earth* (Jamiroquai)

24   *Hormonally Yours* (1995)

25   Red Hot Chili Peppers

26   The Charlatans

27   'Mmmbop' – Hanson

28   *Definitely Maybe*

29   Death Row Records

30   Sonia (also recorded by Kylie Minogue)

31   Candy Flip

32   'The Most Beautiful Girl In The World' (1994)

33   Bob Dylan

34   1993 (March)

35   'I Got The...'

36   Melanie C (her hilarious version of the lyrics was "I am an Antichrist, I am Sporty Spice")

37   N.W.A

38   Shanks & Bigfoot

39   Lenny Kravitz (1991)

40   Roberta Flack (reaching number 6)

Round
21

Name The Hit *Part 2*

Name the song these classic first lines come from:

1
" *Never saw it as the start,*
it's more a change of heart "

2
" Indians send signals from
the rocks above the pass "

3
" Just before our love got lost
you said, "I am as constant as a northern star" "

4
" You fill up my senses "

5
" *Your knuckles*
whiten on the wheel "

6
" Lovin' you isn't the right thing to do "

7
" *Young teacher, the subject of*
school girl fantasy "

8

"Jojo was a man who thought he was a loner, but he knew it couldn't last"

9

I was happy in the haze of a drunken hour

10

"I love you from the bottom of my pencil case"

11

"There's something happening here and what it is ain't exactly clear"

12

Here comes Johnny Yen again with the liquor and drugs

13

I'll protect you from the hooded claw, keep the vampires from your door

14

"There lived a certain man in Russia long ago"

15

"Dealers keep dealin', thieves keep thievin', whores keep whorin', junkies keep scorin'"

16 " Whatever happened to Leon Trotsky? "

17 " *Wake up kids, we've got the dreamers disease* "

18 " I heard you on the wireless back in fifty-two "

19 " *When I was young, I'd listen to the radio waiting for my favourite song* "

20 " I used to think that I could not go on and life was nothing but an awful song "

21 " *I'm nothing special, in fact I'm a bit of a bore* "

22 " Six o'clock already, I was just in the middle of a dream "

66 *Confidence is a preference for the habitual voyeur of what is known as...* 99

23

66 Ah here we are, ah here we are, ah here we go 99

24

66 Funny how I find myself in love with you 99

25

66 *When routine bites hard and ambitions are low* 99

26

66 Billy rapped all night about his suicide 99

27

66 Jitterbug, jitterbug, jitterbug, jitterbug 99

28

Name The Hit Part 2

29 "*Sometimes I feel like I don't have a partner*"

30 "Well no-one told me about her, the way she lied"

31 "Stuck inside these four walls, sent inside forever"

32 "*Old pirates yes they rob I, sold I to the merchant ships*"

33 "There she was just walking down the street..."

34 "*You say I only hear what I want to*"

Name The Hit Part 2

66 *Looking out the door I see the rain fall upon the funeral mourners* 99

35

66 *I am not in love, but I'm open to persuasion…* 99

36

66 Didn't I make you feel like you were the only man? 99

37

66 Even through the darkest phase, be it thick or thin 99

38

66 *In one single moment your whole life can turn round* 99

39

66 *Please could you stop the noise, I'm trying to get some rest* 99

40

Round
21

Answers

Name The Hit | Rock & Pop Quiz Book

1 'The Day We Caught The Train' (Ocean Colour Scene, from *Moseley Shoals*, 1995)

2 'Cool For Cats' (Squeeze, from *Cool For Cats*, 1979)

3 'A Case Of You' (Joni Mitchell, from *Blue*, 1971, also covered by Diana Krall)

4 'Annie's Song' (John Denver, from *The Best Of John Denver*, 1974)

5 'Made Of Stone' (The Stone Roses, from *The Stone Roses*, 1990, originally released in 1989)

6 'Go Your Own Way' (Fleetwood Mac, from *Rumours*, 1977)

7 'Don't Stand So Close To Me' (The Police, from *Zenyatta Mondatta*, 1980)

8 'Get Back' (The Beatles, from *Let It Be*, 1969)

9 'Heaven Knows I'm Miserable Now' (The Smiths, from *Hatful Of Hollow*, 1984)

10 'Song For Whoever' (Beautiful South, from *Welcome To The Beautiful South*, 1989)

11 'For What It's Worth' (Buffalo Springfield, from *Buffalo Springfield*, 1967)

12 'Lust For Life' (Iggy Pop, from *Lust For Life*, 1977)

13 'The Power Of Love' (Frankie Goes To Hollywood, from *Welcome To The Pleasure Dome*, 1984)

14 'Rasputin' (Boney M, from *Night Flight To Venus*, 1978)

15 'Rocks' (Primal Scream, from *Give Out But Don't Give Up*, 1994)

16 'No More Heroes' (The Stranglers, from *No More Heroes*, 1977)

17 'You Get What You Give' (The New Radicals, from *Maybe You've Been Brainwashed Too*, 1999)

18 'Video Killed The Radio Star' (Buggles, from *The Age Of Plastic*, 1979)

19 'Yesterday Once More' (The Carpenters, from *Now And Then* 1973)

20 'I Believe I Can Fly' (R Kelly, from *R*, 1997)

21 'Thank You For The Music' (ABBA, from *Thank You For The Music*, 1983)

22 'Manic Monday' (The Bangles, from *Different Light* – 1986 originally written by Prince under the pseudonym Christopher)

23 'Parklife' (Blur, from *Parklife*, 1994)

24 'Rockin' All Over The World' (Status Quo, from *Rockin' All Over The World*, 1977)

25 'It's My Life' (Talk Talk, from *It's My Life*, 1984, covered by No Doubt, 2003)

26 'Love Will Tear Us Apart' (Joy Division, from *Closer*, 1980)

27 'All The Young Dudes' (Mott The Hoople, from *All The Young Dudes*, 1972, written and produced by David Bowie)

28 'Wake Me Up Before You Go-Go' (Wham!, from *Make It Big*, 1984)

29 'Under The Bridge' (Red Hot Chili Peppers, from *BloodSugarSexMagik*, 1992, re-issued in 1994)

30 'She's Not There' (The Zombies, 1964)

31 'Band On The Run' (Paul McCartney & Wings, from *Band On The Run*, 1974)

32 'Redemption Song' (Bob Marley, from *Uprising*, 1980)

33 'Do Wah Diddy Diddy' (Manfred Mann, 1964, originally recorded by The Exciters in 1961)

34 'Stay (I Missed You)' (Lisa Loeb, from *Tails*, 1994)

35 'Lover, You Should've Come Over' (Jeff Buckley, from *Grace*, 1994)

36 'Love And Affection' (Joan Armatrading, from *Joan Armatrading*, 1976)

37 '(Take A Little) Piece Of My Heart' (Erma Franklin, 1967)

38 'Constant Craving' (k d lang, from *Ingenue*, 1992)

39 'Dry Your Eyes' (The Streets, from *A Grand Don't Come For Free*, 2004)

40 'Paranoid Android' (Radiohead, from *OK Computer*, 1997)

Round
22

The 2000s *Part 2*

1   *Which single was the 1000th number 1*
    to top the UK charts in 2005?

2   *Which two colours are associated with* **U2**
    for their album How to Dismantle An
    Atomic Bomb, *and customised iPod?*

3   *Who played the piano on* **Band Aid 20**'s *version of*
    'Do They Know It's Christmas?'

4   *Who was the winner of the Best British Male Solo*
    Artist award at 2004's Brit Awards ceremony?

5   *What did the* **Pixies** *call their*
    Best Of album, released in 2004?

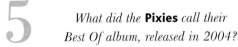

6   *Which American rock singer featured on*
    'Let Me Blow Ya Mind' by **Eve** *in 2001?*

7   *Which Pink Floyd song did*
    Scissor Sisters *cover in 2004?*

Whose 2001 debut album is entitled
All Killer No Filler?

What is the name of **Britney Spears'** *third UK*
number 1 single?

In 2000, **Robbie Williams** *won two Brit*
Awards for Best British Single and Best British
Video, for which song?

What is on the cover of
Coldplay's Parachutes?

Which French band is name-checked in the title
of **LCD Soundsystem**'s *2005 single '_____*
_____ Is Playing At My House'?

Which singer is featured on **Chicane**'s *'Don't*
Give Up', reaching number 1 in 2000?

What was **Madonna**'s *2003*
number 1 album called?

Which BBC cartoon character made it to the
Christmas number 1 spot in 2000?

16 *Which singer-songwriter did jazzer* **Diana Krall** *marry in 2003?*

17 *Who is the featured vocalist on the single 'Scorpio Rising' by* **Death In Vegas***?*

18 *Who originally sang the chorus on 'Dry Your Eyes' by* **The Streets***, but asked for his version not to be used on the final release?*

19 *Which* **Electric Six** *song was originally released in the US in 2001 under their former name, The Wild Bunch?*

20 *Which* **Dido** *song did* **Eminem** *sample in 'Stan'?*

21 *Who duetted with* **Will Young** *on a cover of* **The Beatles***' 'The Long And Winding Road', which reached number one in 2002?*

22 *Which popular singer/pianist is featured on* **OutKast***'s 'Take Off Your Cool Things' from* Speakerboxxx/The Love Below, *in 2003?*

Whose 2003 album is entitled
De-Loused In The Comatorium?

23

Which album did **Massive Attack**
release in 2003, reaching number 1
in the UK album charts?

24

Which band was formed by the losers of the very
first Pop Stars *TV show in the UK?*

25

Which 80s song did
George Michael *sample on his*
single 'Shoot The Dog' 2003?

26

With which rock super-group did
Britney Spears *appear at*
Superbowl 35 in 2001?

27

Songs by which UK artist are the basis for the
2003 musical Tonight's The Night?

28

29

*Which **Talk Talk** song did **No Doubt** cover in 2003?*

30

Who won the 2003 Mobo Award for Best RnB act?

31

*Which **Robbie Williams** single is based on the **Barry White** song 'It's Ecstasy When You Lay Down Next To Me'?*

32

***The Darkness** won three categories at the 2004 Brit Awards, what were they?*

33

Which band won the Best Live Act Award in the 2005 Brit Awards?

34

*What tattoo does **Pete Doherty** show on the inside of his arm on **The Libertines**' eponymous album?*

Who co-wrote and recorded the song 'Where Is My Boy' with electronica outfit **Faultline**?

35

Which song by **Red Hot Chili Peppers** *did* **Crazy Town** *sample in their number three single 'Butterfly'?*

36

Which band consists of **Tom Chaplin**, **Tim Rice-Oxley** *and* **Richard Hughes**?

37

From which 2002 singer-songwriter's debut album does the song 'Cheers Darlin'' come?

38

Which **Bee Gees** *song did* **Destiny's Child** *cover in 2001, reaching number 3 in the UK charts?*

39

Who topped the UK singles charts in April 2004 with 'F**k It (I Don't Want You Back)'?

40

1   'One Night' by Elvis Presley (originally a number 1 hit in 1959)

2   Red and black

3   Thom Yorke

4   Daniel Bedingfield

5   *Wave Of Mutilation*

6   Gwen Stefani

7   'Comfortably Numb'

8   Sum 41

9   'Oops... I Did It Again' (2000)

10   'She's The One'

11   A yellow globe

12   Daft Punk ('Daft Punk Is Playing At My House')

13   Bryan Adams

14   *American Life*

15   Bob The Builder (with 'Can We Fix It')

16   Elvis Costello (they co-wrote songs on Krall's album *The Girl In The Other Room*)

17   Liam Gallagher (2002)

18   Chris Martin

19   'Danger! High Voltage'

20   'Thank You'

21   Gareth Gates

22   Norah Jones

23   The Mars Volta

24   *100th Window*

25   Liberty X (the X was added later as there was already an American group called Liberty. Liberty X have since become more successful than the winners of the competition Hear'Say)

26   'Love Action (I Believe In Love)' Human League

27   Aerosmith

28   Rod Stewart

29   'It's My Life'

30   Justin Timberlake

31   'Rock DJ'

32   Best British Group, Best British Album (*Permission To Land*) and Best British Rock Act

33   Muse

34   A skull and crossbones

35   Chris Martin (from the album *Your Love Means Everything*)

36   'Pretty Little Ditty' (2001)

37   Keane

38   *O* (Damien Rice)

39   'Emotion'

40   Eamon

Pop Trivia *Part 5*

1   *What is the longest number 1 hit
in rock history?*

2   *Which single surpassed **Bing Crosby**'s
'White Christmas' to become the
best selling single ever?*

3   *The first ever double albums were
both released in mid-1966 – name both albums
and artists, and what did the two albums'
closing tracks have in common?*

4   *Which rock act has won the Q award for Best Act In
The World Today a massive four times?*

5   ***Queen**'s 'Bohemian Rhapsody' was
number 1 in 1975. It reached the top spot
again as a double A-side with 'These Are
The Days Of Our Lives' in which year?*

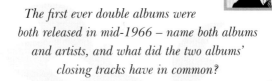

6   *Which was the first British group
to top the US charts, and with what song?*

7   *Apart from **Hendrix** himself, name
the three other celebrities immortalized in
puppet form on the original British sleeve
for Jimi's **Band Of Gypsys** album?*

8   *Who originally recorded 'Mistletoe & Wine'?*

9

Who replaced **Ozzy Osbourne**
as lead singer of **Black Sabbath**
in 1978?

10

Which 1948 **Betty Hutton** *tune did* **Björk**
cover on her album, Post?

11

Which artist is hidden in this anagram?
ARCHLY EARS

12

What is **Jackie Wilson***'s only UK
number 1 hit?*

13

In what year did Epic records release
Michael Jackson*'s album,* Thriller?

14

What is the name of **Madonna***'s record label?*

15

What instrument did **Sting** *play
in* **The Police***?*

16

*Which song, later to become a
huge hit, was originally the B-side to the single
'Train To Nowhere'?*

17

*Which artist was the creator
of the legendary 'duckwalk'?*

Pop Trivia Part 5

18 *Which video was the very first to be aired on MTV in 1981?*

19 *The parental advisory sticker was introduced as a result of the US government's reaction to which* **Prince** *song?*

20 *Who played the piano on the* **Shangri-La**'s *1965 hit, 'Leader of the Pack'?*

21 *Which song was the first to feature a 'fade-in' beginning?*

22 *Who are the famous fathers of the singers in* **Wilson Philips**?

23 *Which songwriter has written the books* And The Ass Saw The Angel *and* King Ink?

24 *Which actress appeared in the video of 'Wicked Game' by* **Chris Isaak**?

25 *Which successful song writing duo have written under the pseudonyms Tripe and Onions, Ann Orson and Carte Blanche amongst others?*

26 *For which event was the* **Freddie Mercury** *and* **Montserrat Caballé** *single 'Barcelona' released?*

Pop Trivia Part 5

How many number 1 albums have
Erasure *had?*

27

Which record label are **The Pixies** *on?*

28

Who won the Brit award for
Best International album in 2003?

29

What does **Clannad** *mean*
in Gaelic?

30

The UK has won the Eurovision song contest
five times. Name the winning songs and artists.

31

What is the band **King Adora** *named after?*

32

Which is the only non-compilation album by
The Smiths *to go to number 1 in the*
UK album charts?

33

Which album by **The Propellerheads**
is currently the longest one-word
album title with 26 letters?

34

Which British female artist won the
Q Classic Songwriter award in 2001?

35

Round
23

Pop Trivia Part 5

36 *Which diva was originally offered 'Son Of A Preacher Man' before* **Dusty Springfield** *made it a hit?*

37 *'Music To Watch Girls Go By' was originally written to advertise which product?*

38 *On which classic novel is* **Jefferson Airplane***'s single 'White Rabbit' based?*

39 *Which album/band won the 1995 Mercury Music Prize?*

40 *What does* **The KLF** *stand for?*

41 *Which song by* **The Chiffons** *did* **George Harrison** *steal from for his song 'My Sweet Lord'?*

42 *Who replaced* **Keith Moon** *after his death as the drummer in* **The Who**?

43 *Who originally recorded 'I Don't Want To Talk About It', later a number 1 hit for* **Rod Stewart***, and a number 3 hit for* **Everything But The Girl**?

What does **R.E.M.** *stand for?*

44

What was the name of
Johnny Cash's *debut album,*
released by Sun Records in 1957?

45

What event caused **Curtis Mayfield**
to be paralysed?

46

With whom did Jennifer Saunders and Joanna
Lumley collaborate on the
charity single 'Absolutely Fabulous'?

47

In which **Oasis** *song does* **Noel Gallagher**
crib bits from 'How Sweet To Be An Idiot'
by **Neil Innes**?

48

Who produced, and drummed
on **Frida**'s *(Lyngstad-Fredriksl*
–Andersson) first solo single
*post-***ABBA**?

49

Which book was the inspiration behind the name
Joy Division?

50

Answers

1 'American Pie' (Don McLean, it lasts 8 minutes and 32 seconds)

2 'Candle In The Wind' by Elton John (helped by being performed at the funeral of Diana Princess of Wales)

3 Bob Dylan – *Blonde On Blonde* and The Mothers Of Invention – *Freak Out!* (The final tracks of both albums took up a whole side of vinyl each, 'Sad Eyed Lady Of The Lowlands' concluding *Blonde On Blonde* is over one 11 minute 20 second side, 'The Return Of The Son Of Monster Magnet' climaxing *Freak Out!* over a whopping 12 minutes 17 seconds)

4 U2 (in 1991 they shared the title with R.E.M.)

5 1991 (released after Freddie Mercury's death to help raise funds for the AIDS charities)

6 The Tornados, with 'Telstar' (1962)

7 Bob Dylan, Brian Jones (The Rolling Stones) and DJ John Peel

8 Twiggy (Cliff Richard later took the song to number 1 in 1988)

9 Ronnie James Dio

10 'It's Oh So Quiet'

11 RAY CHARLES

12 'Reet Petite' (re-released in 1986, originally charting at number 6 in 1957)

13 December 1982

14 Maverick

15 The bass

16 'Tequila' by The Champs

17 Chuck Berry (Chuck bopped his head and held his guitar out when he walked about the stage. A member of the audience yelled "Look at that duck!" and the 'duckwalk' was born)

18 'Video Killed The Radio Star' (Buggles)

19 'Darling Nikki' from *Purple Rain* (owing to its reference to female masturbation, 'I guess you could say she was a sex friend, I met her in a hotel lobby masturbating with a magazine')

20 Billy Joel (he was only 16 at the time)

21 'Eight Days A Week' – The Beatles

22 Brian Wilson (Beach Boys) and John Phillips (The Mamas & The Papas) (Owen Elliott, daughter of Mama Cass, was also briefly a member)

23 Nick Cave

24 Helena Christensen

25 Elton John and Bernie Taupin

26 The 1992 Olympic Games in Barcelona

27 Five (*The Innocents* (1988), *Wild!* (1989), *Chorus* (1991), *Pop! The First 20 Hits* (1992), *I Say I Say I Say* (1994))

28 4AD

29 Eminem – *The Eminem Show*

30 Family

31 Sandi Shaw – 'Puppet On A String' (1967), Lulu – 'Boom-Bang-A-Bang' (1969), Brotherhood Of Man – 'Save Your Kisses For Me' (1976), Bucks Fizz – 'Making Your Mind Up' (1981), Katrina And The Waves – 'Love Shine A Light' (1997)

32 A huge vibrator

33 *Meat Is Murder* (1985)

34 *Decksdrumsandrockandroll*

35 Kate Bush

36 Aretha Franklin (though she did record it after Dusty's version had charted)

37 Diet Cola (by the Bob Crewe Generation)

38 *Alice In Wonderland* by Lewis Carroll

39 *Dummy* (Portishead)

40 Kopyright Liberation Fund

41 'He's So Fine' (Harrison was sued for copyright infringement for his number 1 hit due to it's strong similarity to the 1963 hit 'He's So Fine'. He was ordered to pay $587,000 in composer's royalties. To capitalise on the publicity of the lawsuit, The Chiffons recorded their own version of 'My Sweet Lord' in 1975)

42 Kenny Jones (formerly of The Faces)

43 Crazy Horse

44 Rapid Eye Movement

45 *Johnny Cash With His Hot And Blue Guitar* (this was the first LP released by Sun Records)

46 A lighting rig fell on him at an outdoor gig

47 Pet Shop Boys

48 'Whatever'

49 Phil Collins

50 *House Of Dolls* by Ka-tzetnik (in the 1955 novel 'Joy Division' referred to the wing of Nazi Concentration camps where inmates were used by SS Officers as prostitutes)

Printed in China   12/05(57116)